BERNARD WAGNESS
PIANO COURSE

BOOK FIVE

THIS BOOK BEGINS EXACTLY WHERE BOOK
FOUR ENDED.   IT CAN BE USED ALSO
VERY SUCCESSFULLY TO FOLLOW
ANY FOURTH GRADE BOOK

PRICE $1.00

HAROLD FLAMMER, Inc
10 East 43rd Street   New York, N. Y.

TO THE TEACHER:

Book Five supplies the teacher and pupil with a wealth of study material of the highest degree of musical content and variety so planned as to create interest and enthusiasm on the part of the pupil, a factor which is so necessary to successful piano study.

Many pupils will be able to master this book in their fourth year of study. Many other pupils will derive great benefit from this book during their fifth or sixth year of study, depending upon age and industry.

ABSENCE OF GRADE MARKS:

The confusing methods of grade markings on piano books and pieces has long been a source of worry to piano teachers. For this reason grade marks have been kept off the books of the Bernard Wagness Piano Course. The author strongly feels that the teacher alone has the authority to grade a pupil, certainly not a person who has never seen this pupil or heard him play.

THE GOAL OF THE BERNARD WAGNESS PIANO COURSE:

In this course the author has endeavored to supply study material to fit the pupil—not to force the pupil to fit some certain grade marking.

IMPORTANCE OF ADEQUATE MATERIAL:

The average piano student does not have sufficient study material due to the fact that materials are often too difficult and require too long a period of time for preparation. This limits the scope of the student's curriculum and lessens his opportunities for fluent artistic playing.

PLAN OF THE MATERIALS:

The Wagness books are planned to provide the student with ample material lying well within the pupil's ability. In this way reading, rhythm, technic, tone and pedalling are given sufficient drill which eventually will lead to perfection.

PROCEDURE OF MATERIALS:

It is suggested that scale work, keyboard harmony study and etude drill be correlated along with the playing of the pianistically arranged melodies and original compositions and classics. Strive to develop in each pupil a beautiful singing melody tone, the most important essential in piano playing.

> This number is an arranged excerpt from one of the greatest of all symphonies. Play it in a lofty, majestic manner, always striving to cause the melody to sing out distinctly above the surrounding accompaniment.

THEME
from the "Andante" — 5th Symphony

P. I. Tschaikowsky
Arranged by Bernard Wagness

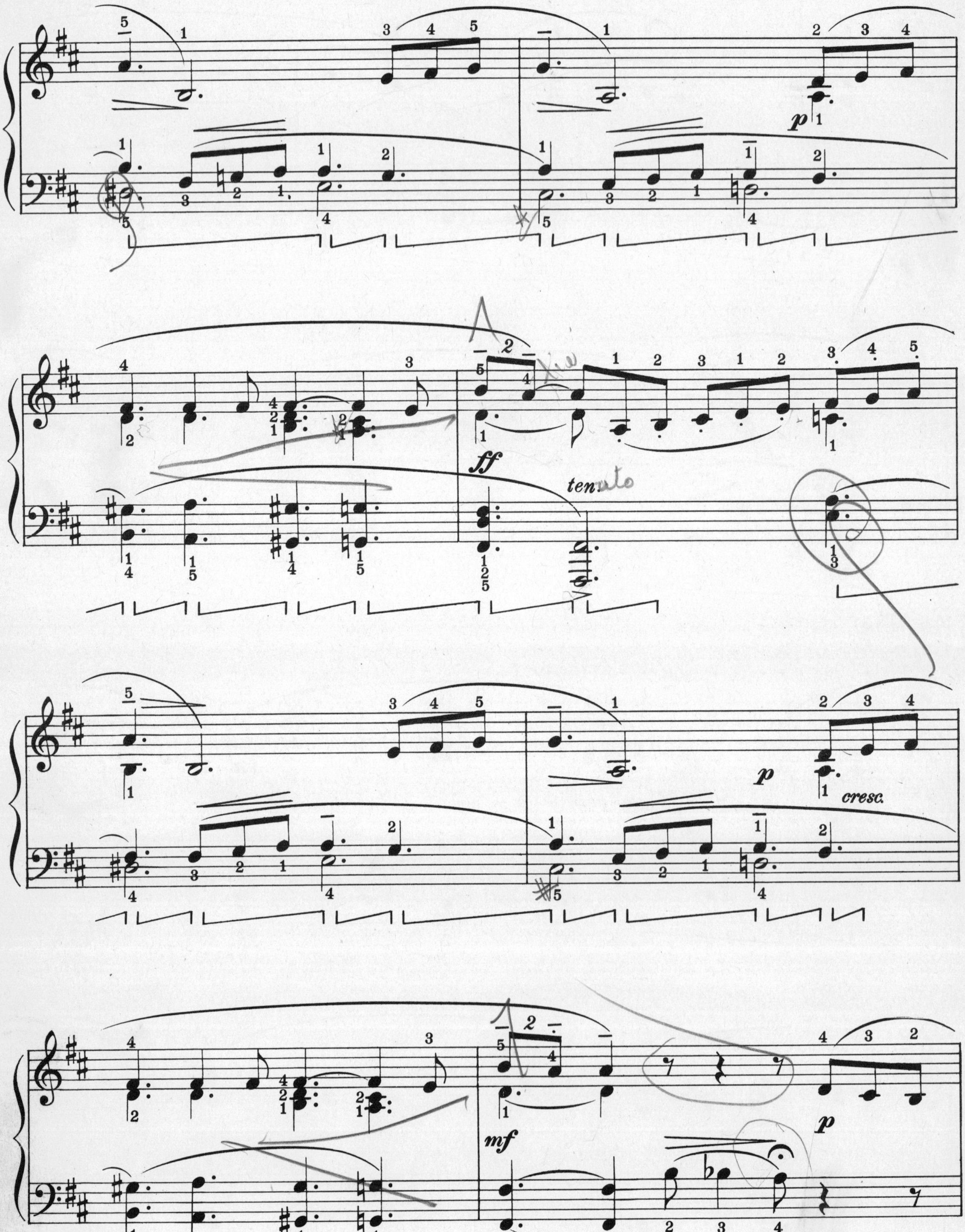
tenuto
cresc.

Più animato

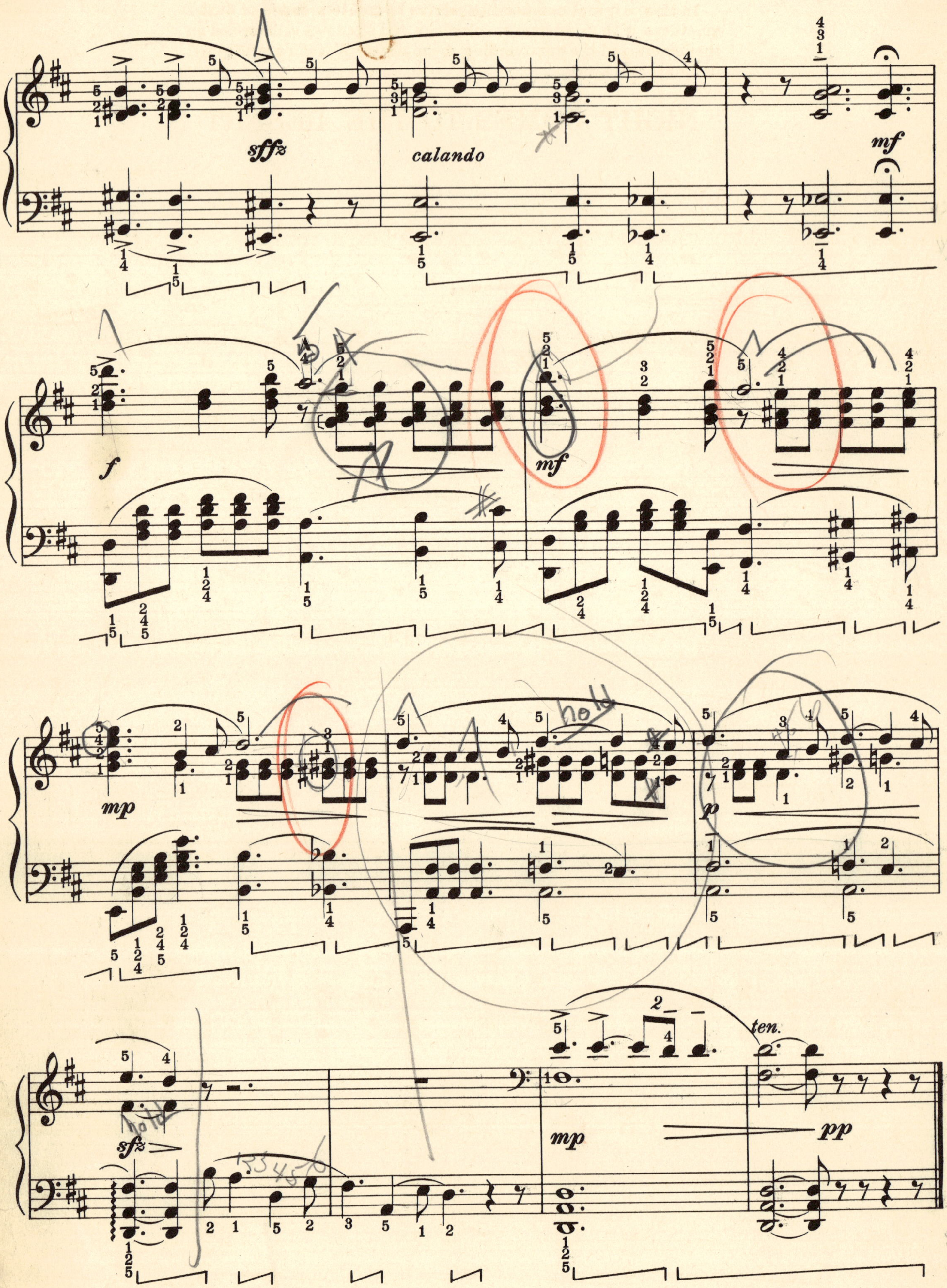
sffz
calando
mf
f
mf
mp
p
sfz
mp
ten.
pp

In this original composition, strive to create a scene of dusky quietness with vivid sunset colorings and shadows silhouetted on the desert and the surrounding mountains. Watch carefully all dynamic markings.

NIGHT COMES TO THE DESERT

Bernard Wagness

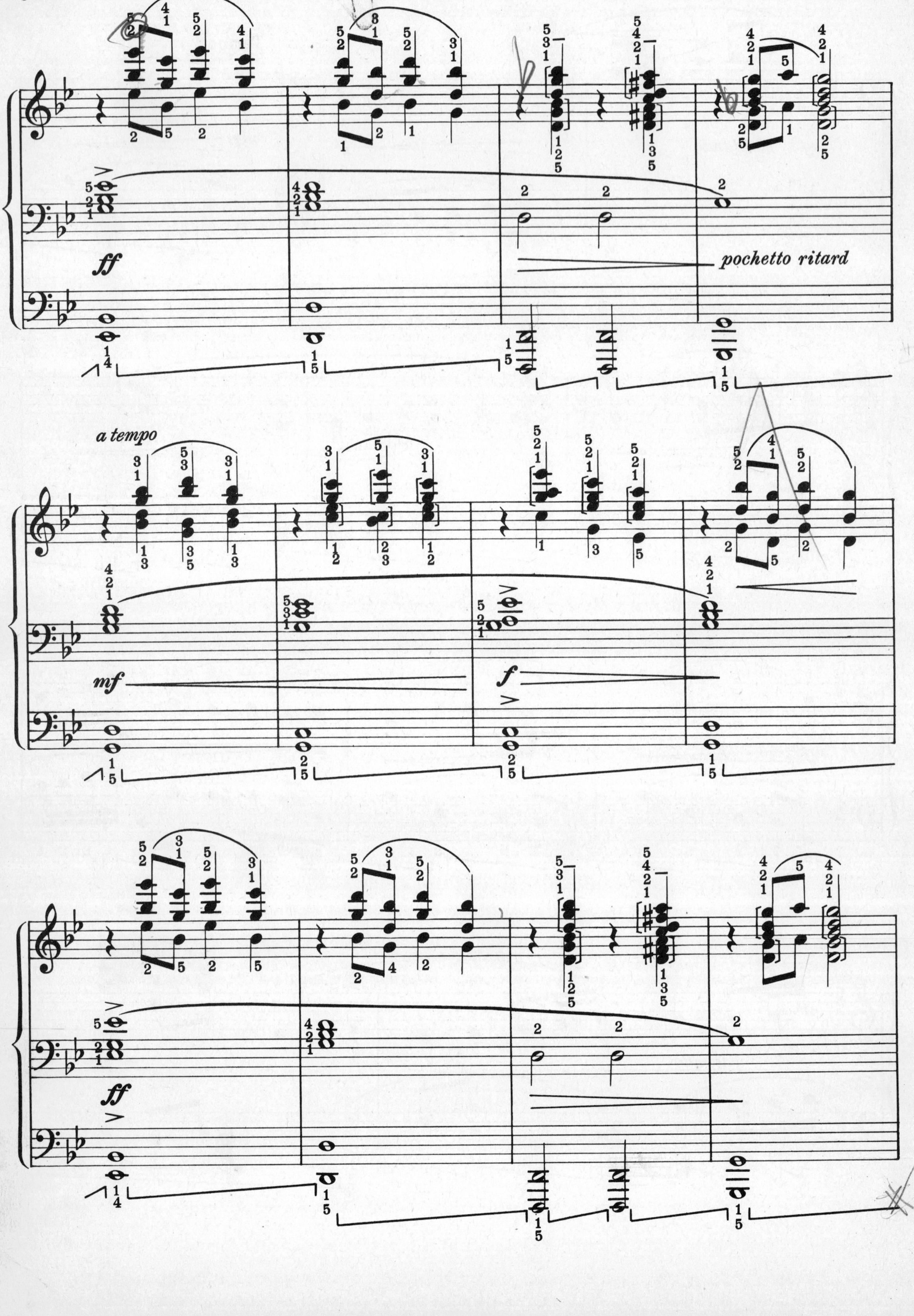
ff
pochetto ritard
a tempo
mf
f
ff

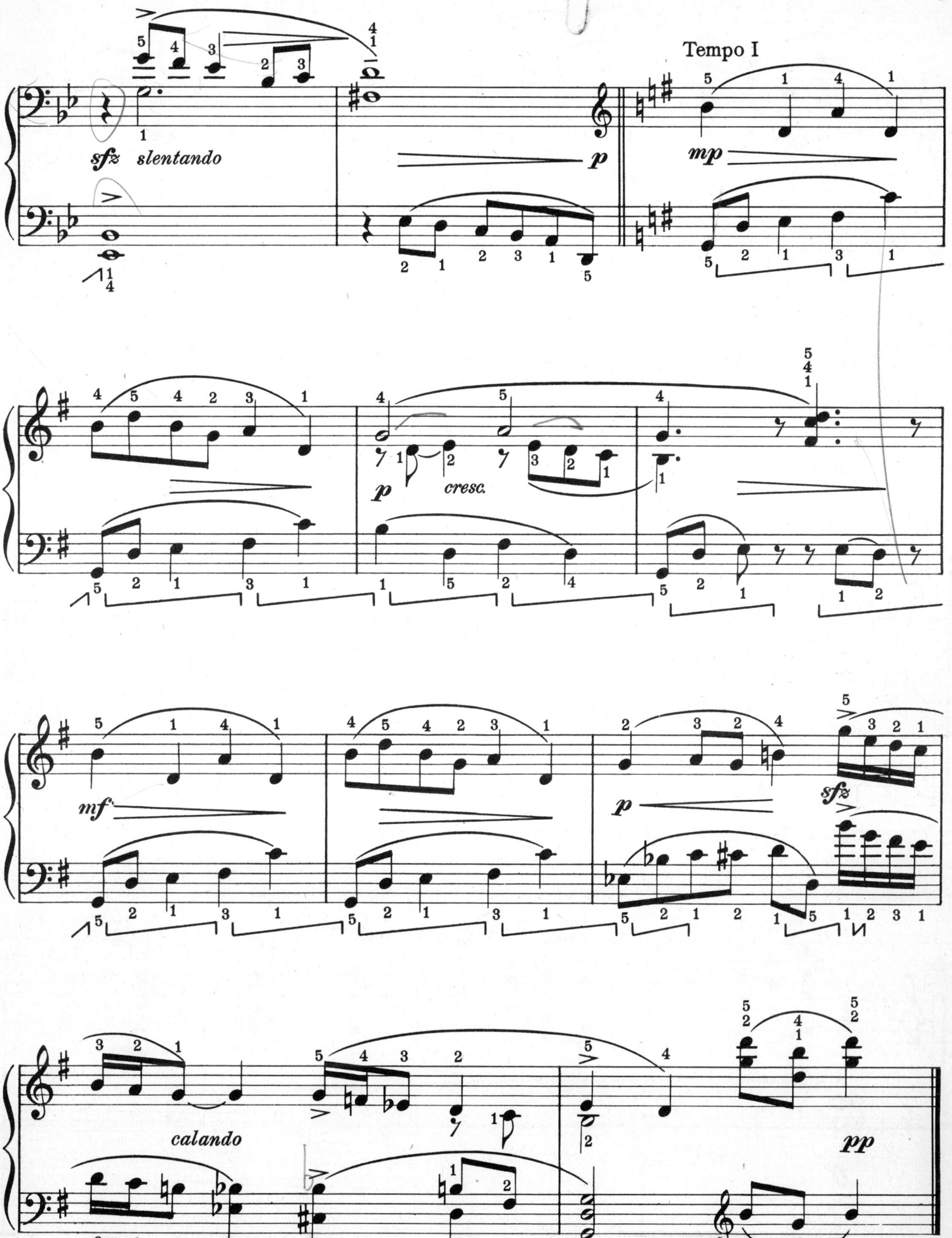
sfz slentando
p
Tempo I
mp
p cresc.
mf
p
sfz
calando
pp

MOMENT MUSICAL

Schubert
Arr. by Bernard Wagness

SCHUBERT

Franz Peter Schubert was born in Vienna January 31, 1797. He studied voice, piano and violin at an early age and soon equalled the skill of his first teachers. At the age of thirteen Schubert started serious composition; at sixteen he wrote his first symphony. Schubert's songs are perhaps the most lofty and inspiring. · He died in 1828.

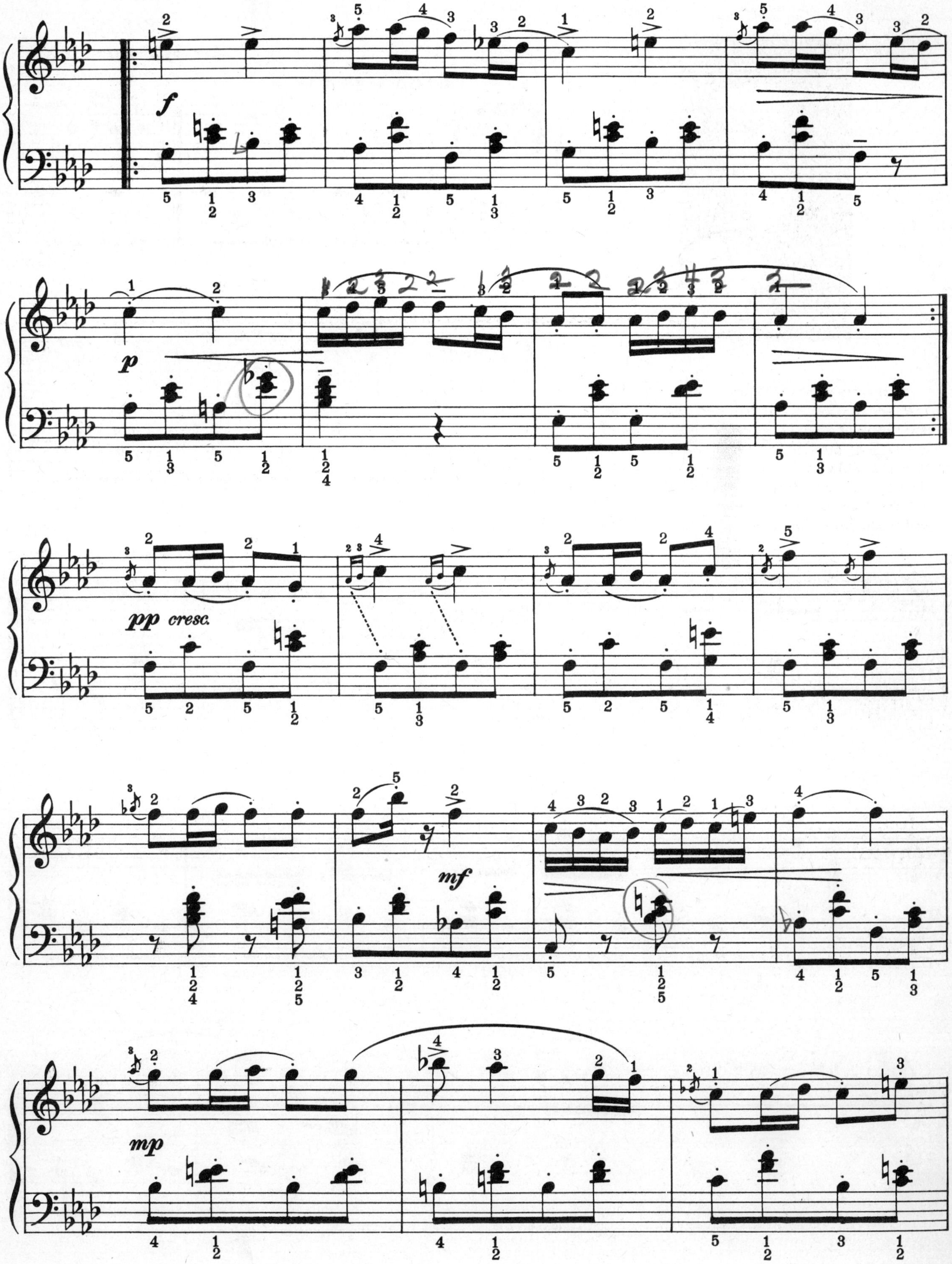
f
p
pp cresc.
mf
mp

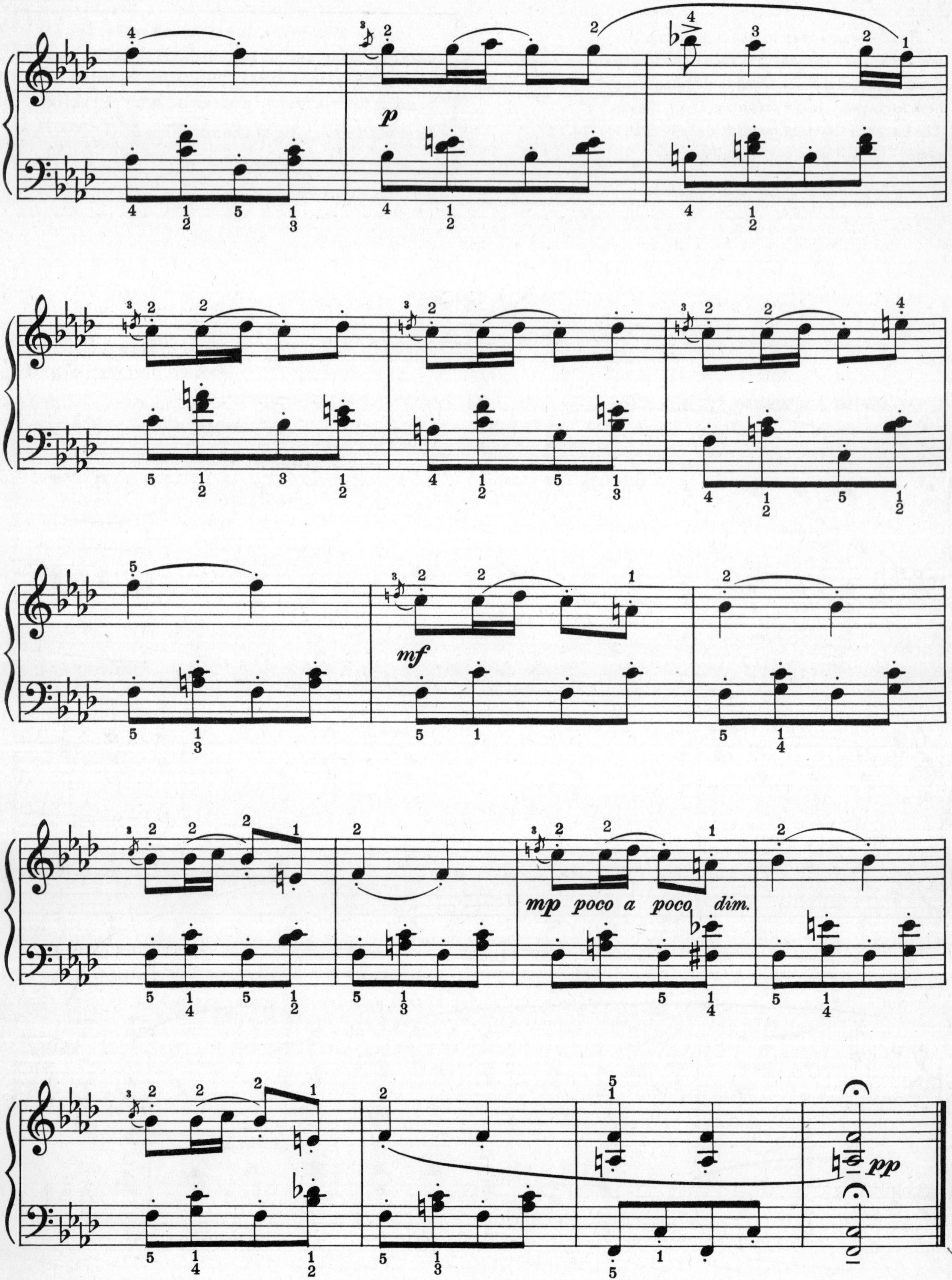
p
mf
mp poco a poco dim.
pp

Handel was a very industrious composer and turned out so many writings and at such great speed, that much of these compositions have been lost. He did write one opera, Xerxes. The Largo is the most popular melody in this opera. Play it very majestically.

Use an arm touch from the shoulder for all chords. Bring out the melody well by using plenty of arm weight for the top voice in patterns similar to that found in measure one. Practice first with a very light thumb. Viz:

LARGO
(From XERXES)

Handel
Arr. by Bernard Wagness

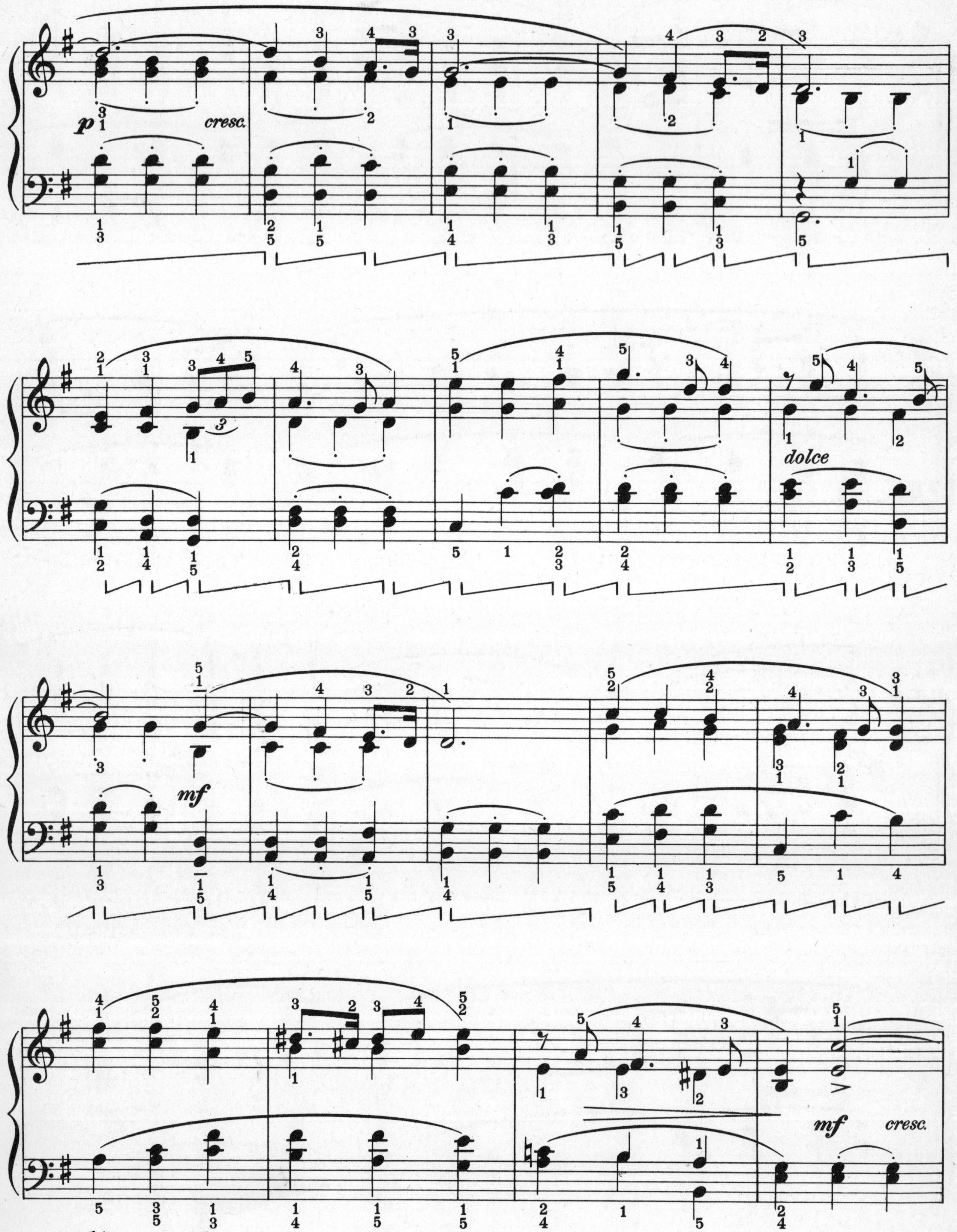
p
cresc.
dolce
mf
mf
cresc.

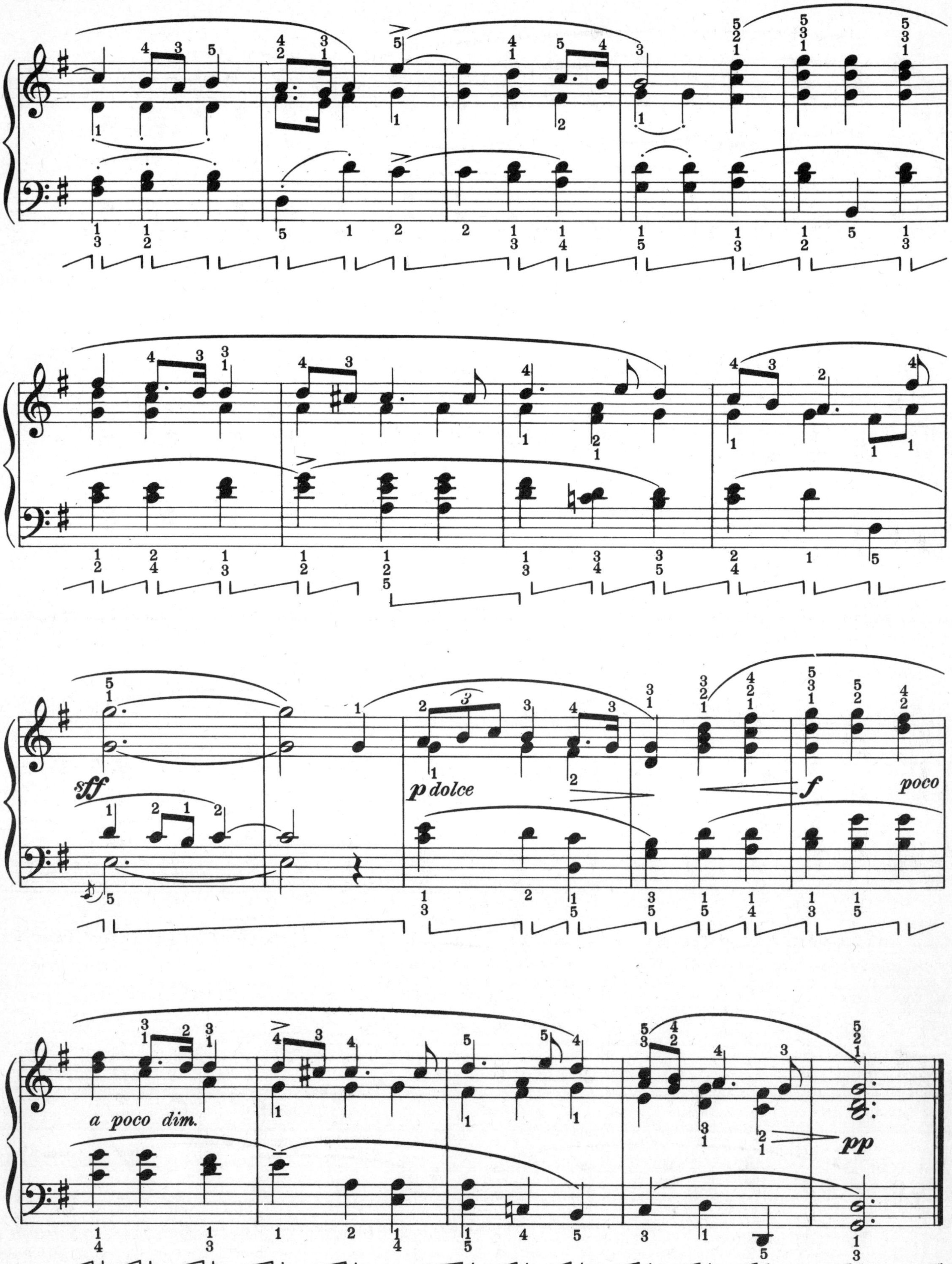
sff
p dolce
f
poco
a poco dim.
pp

Robert Schumann was born in 1810 at Zwuickau, Germany. He showed early signs of great musical talent and after five years of study Schumann started composing music. He then began piano lessons with a very famous teacher, Frederick Wieck, and later married his teacher's daughter, Clara, who also was a remarkably fine pianist. He died July 29, 1856, after a mental breakdown brought on by over-work.

Play this piece with a firm touch, employing sufficient muscular energy in the fingers to produce a forte tone. There must be no stiffness in the wrist. Observe the cap accents and the *sfz* markings. Do not rush the tempo, as stiffness in the wrists and in the arm may result.

KNIGHT RUPERT
Op. 68, №12

R. Schumann

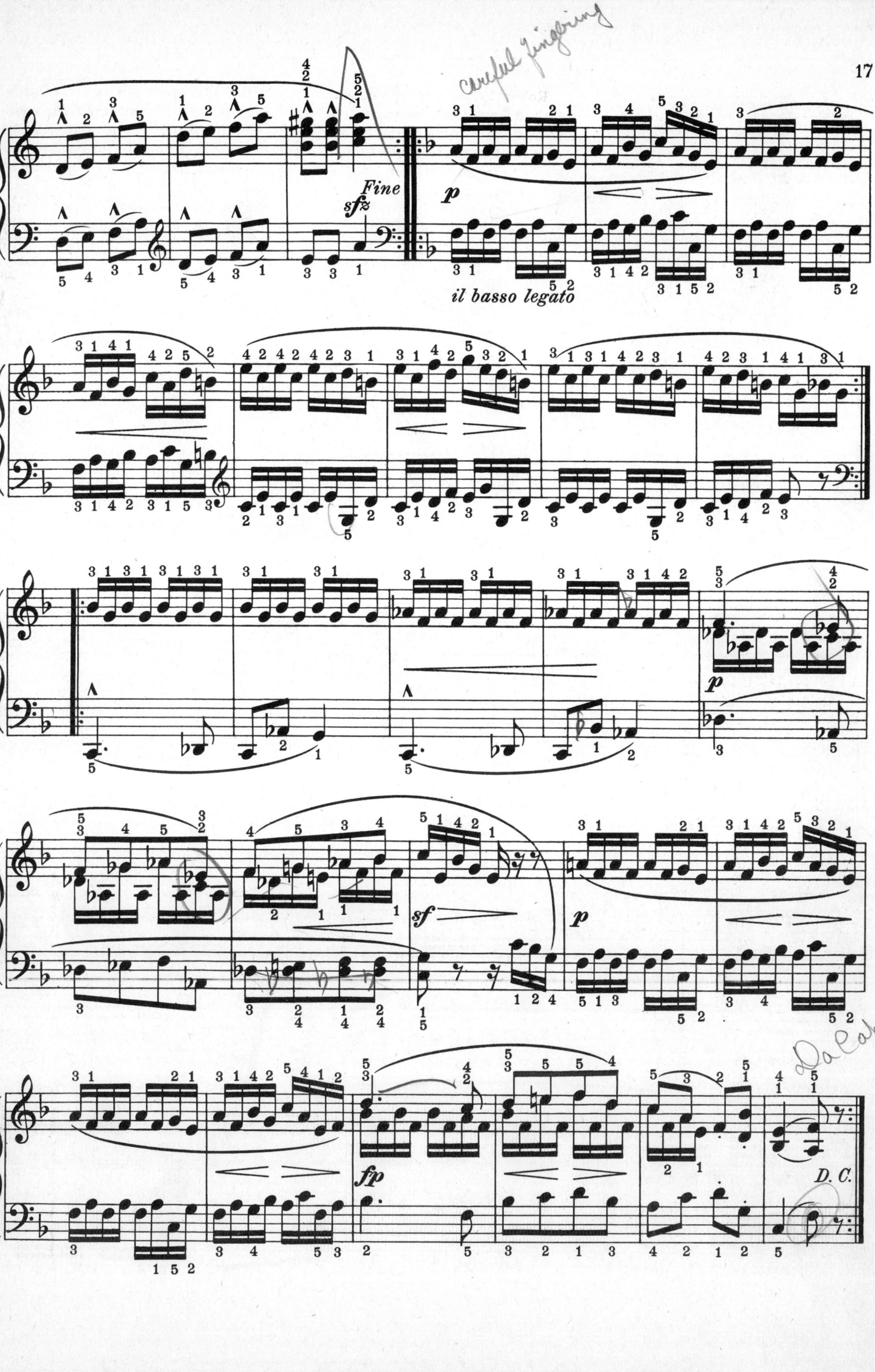
careful fingering
Fine
sfz
p
il basso legato
sf
fp
D. C.
Da Capo

This musical etude weaves back and forth from C major to C minor aided by the diminished seventh chord (VII⁹). Block all broken chord patterns at first into solid chord groups and analyze each chord.

HARP PRELUDE IN C MAJOR

Bernard Wagness

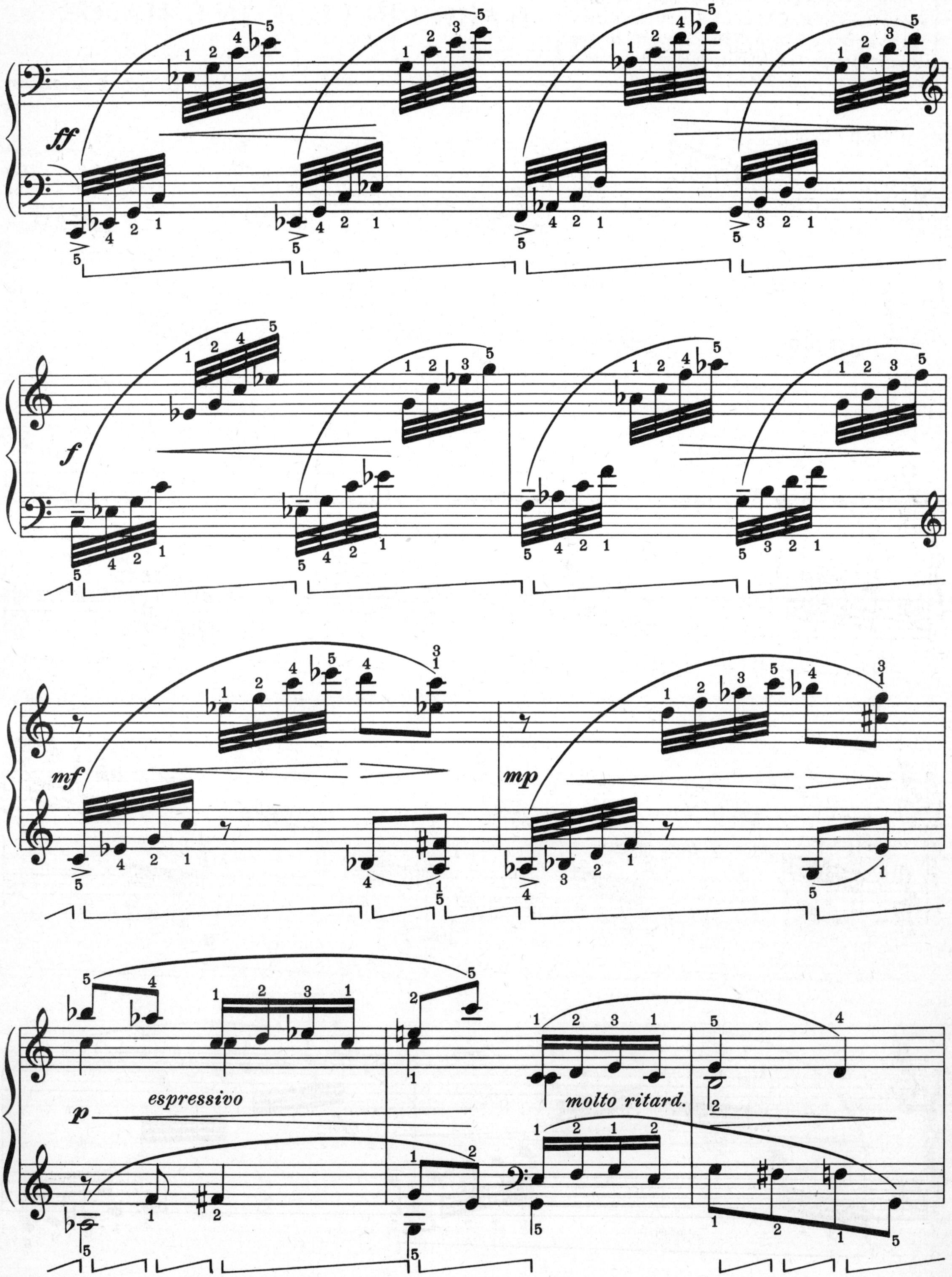
ff
f
mf
mp
p
espressivo
molto ritard.

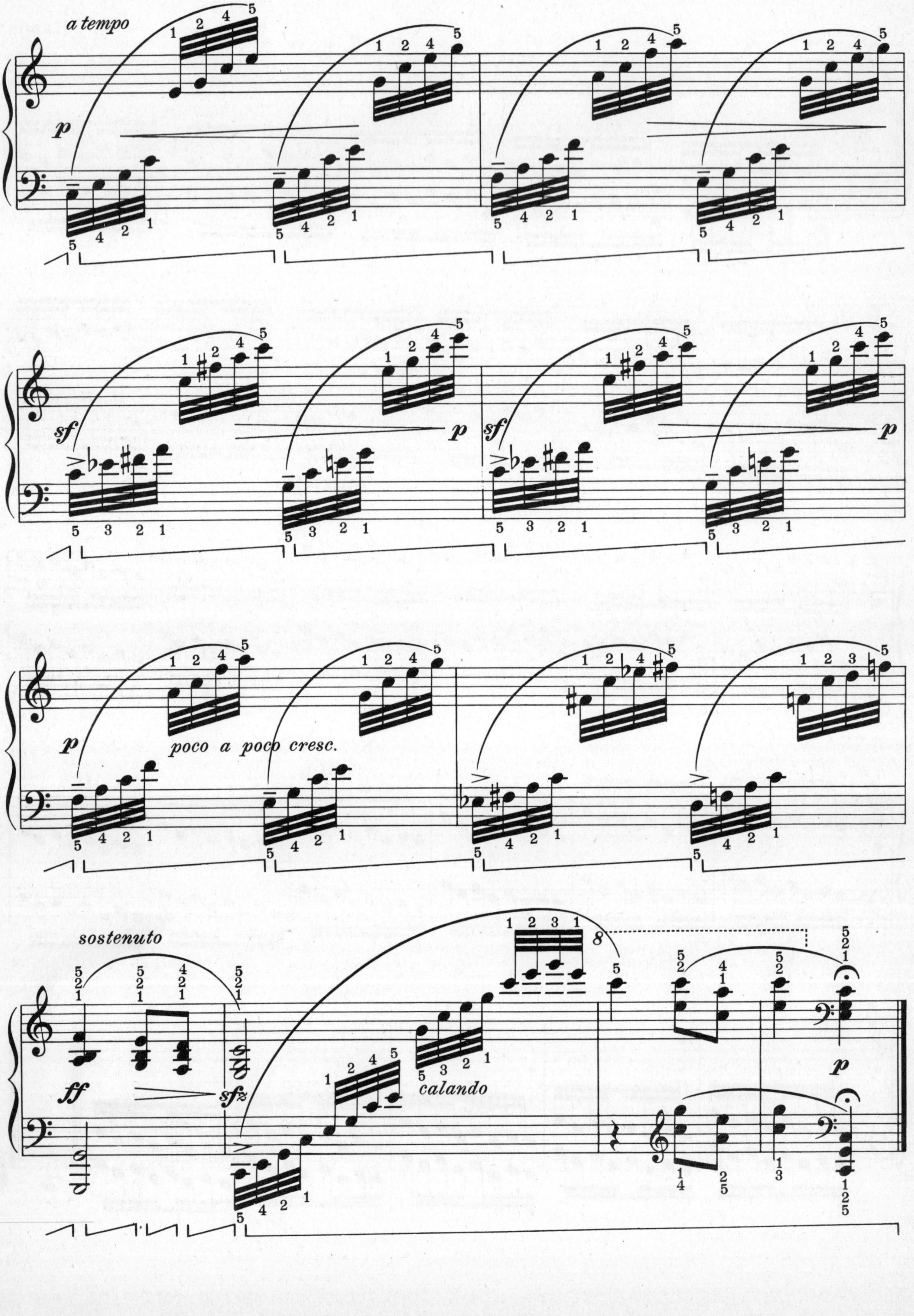
a tempo
poco a poco cresc.
sostenuto
calando

THE QUAKING ASPEN

Hanon

DETERMINATION

Heller

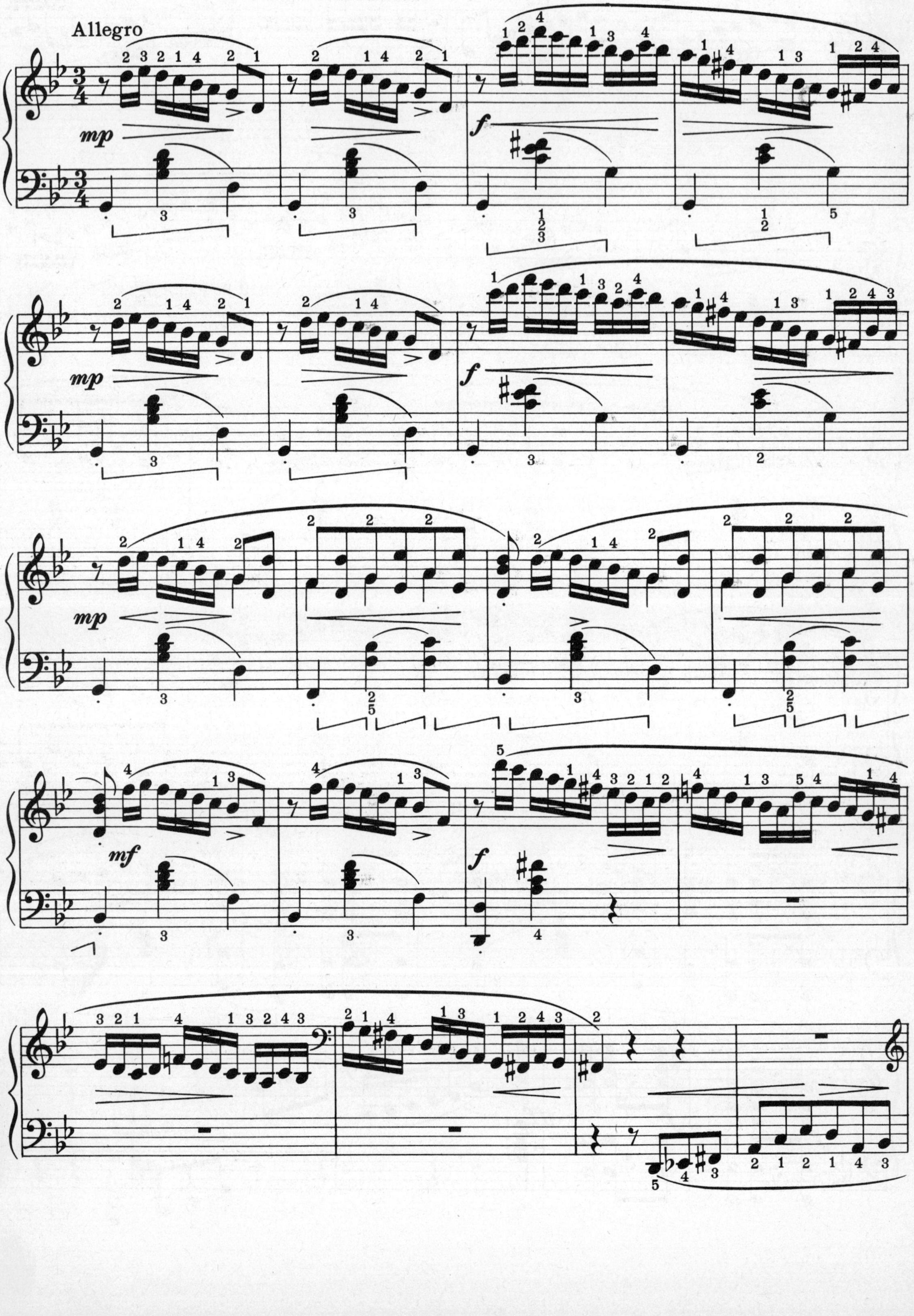

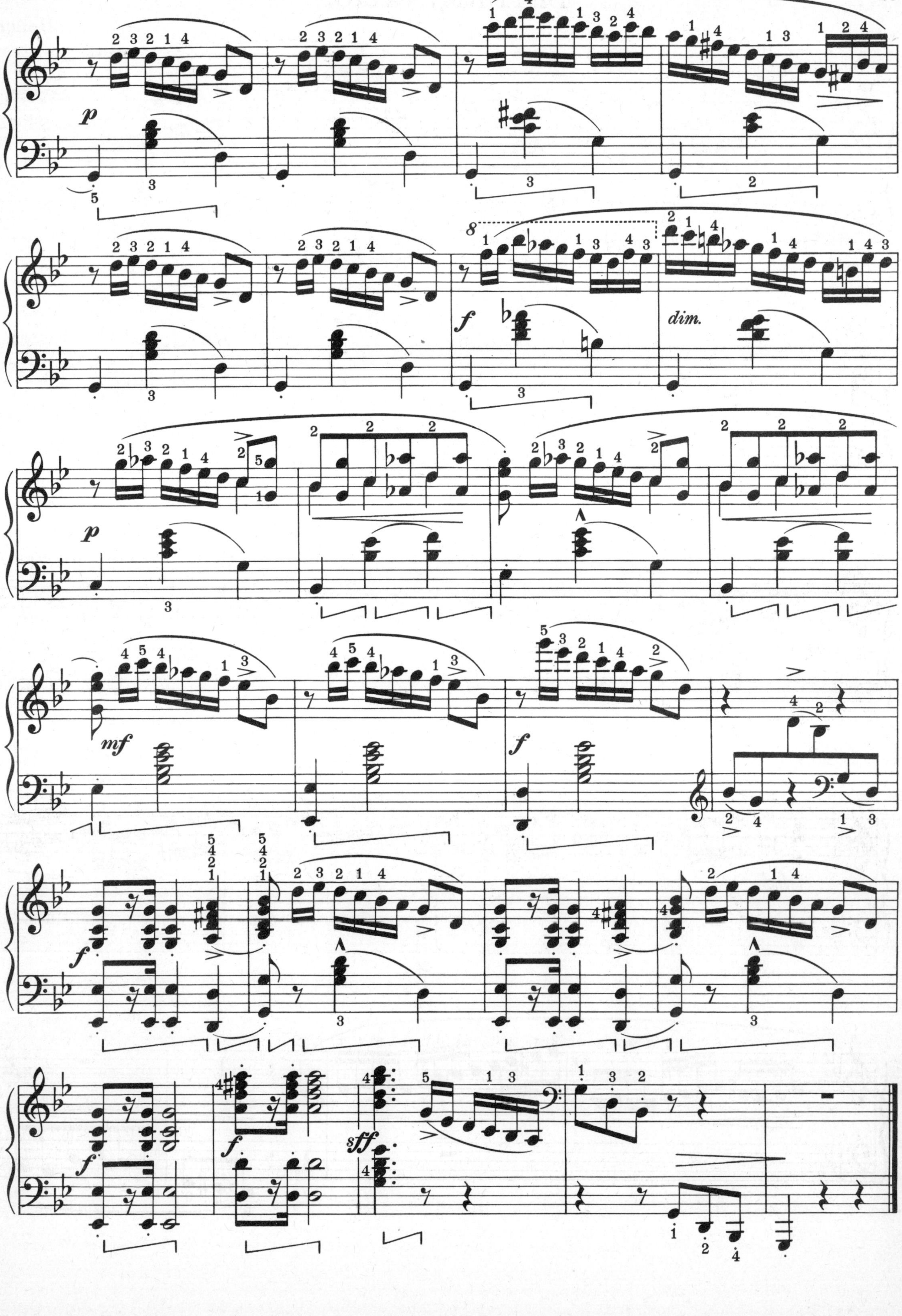
p
f
dim.
p
mf
f
f
f
f
sff

A study in passage sixths employing hinge-wrist action in either
hand. With an erect, firm fifth finger, as in Figure A, and a slightly
bent organized thumb, as in Figure B, raise the hand, as in Figure C
and then allow the hand to drop upon the keyboard, as in Figure A.
In this up and down hinge action, originating at the wrist, the forearm
must remain quiet and balanced. Continue the exaggerated hinge
action until control is established, when the speed should be increased
and the wrist action reduced.

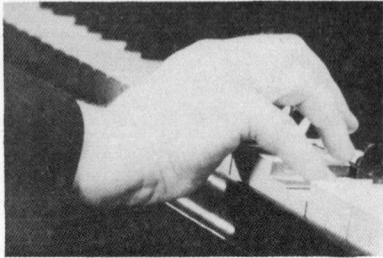

Figure A

Figure B

Figure C

A FROSTY MORNING

Bernard Wagness

Capriccetto

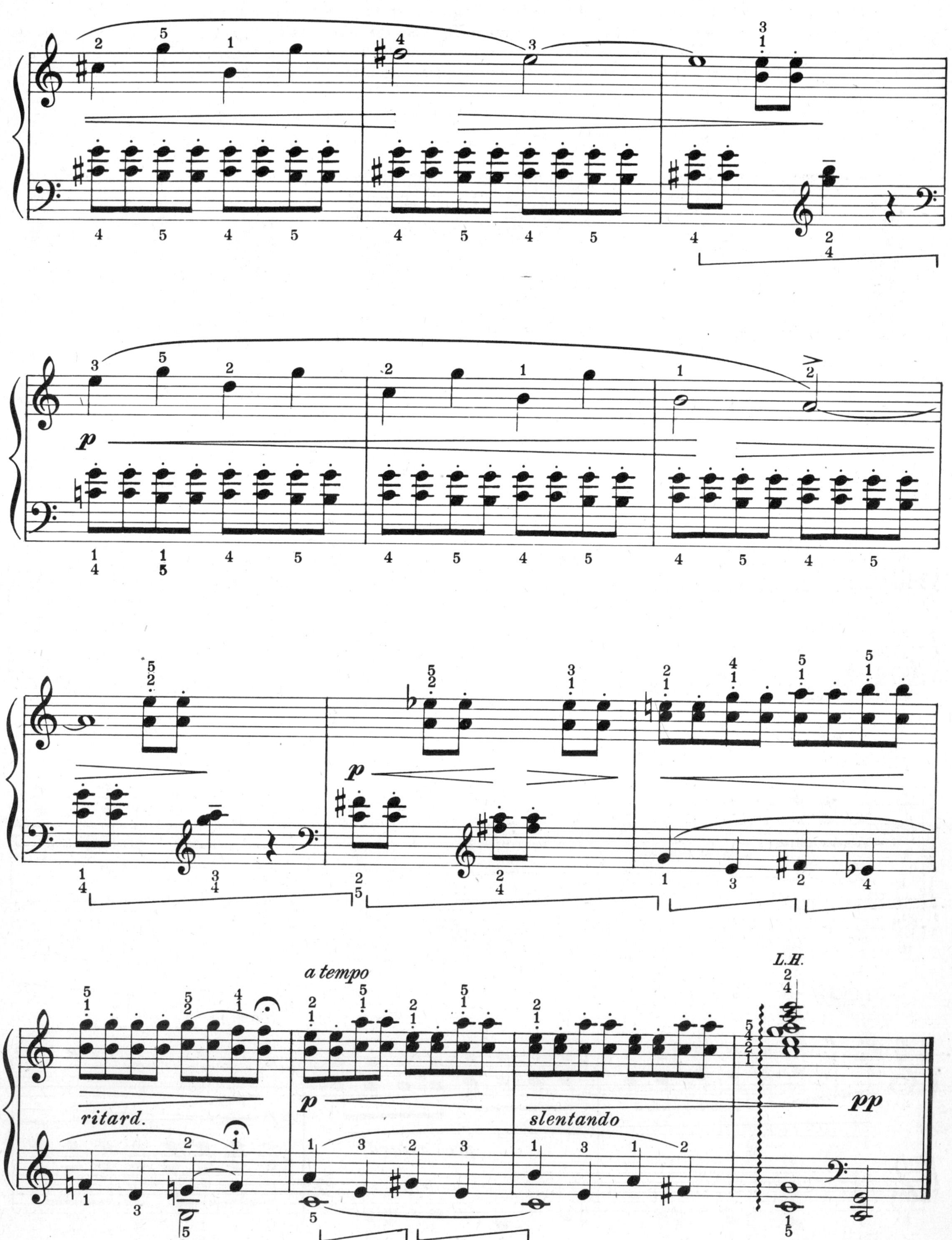
p
p
ritard.
a tempo
p
slentando
L.H.
pp

THE BLUE DANUBE WALTZ

Johann Strauss, Jr.
Arranged by Bernard Wagness

Grazioso delicato

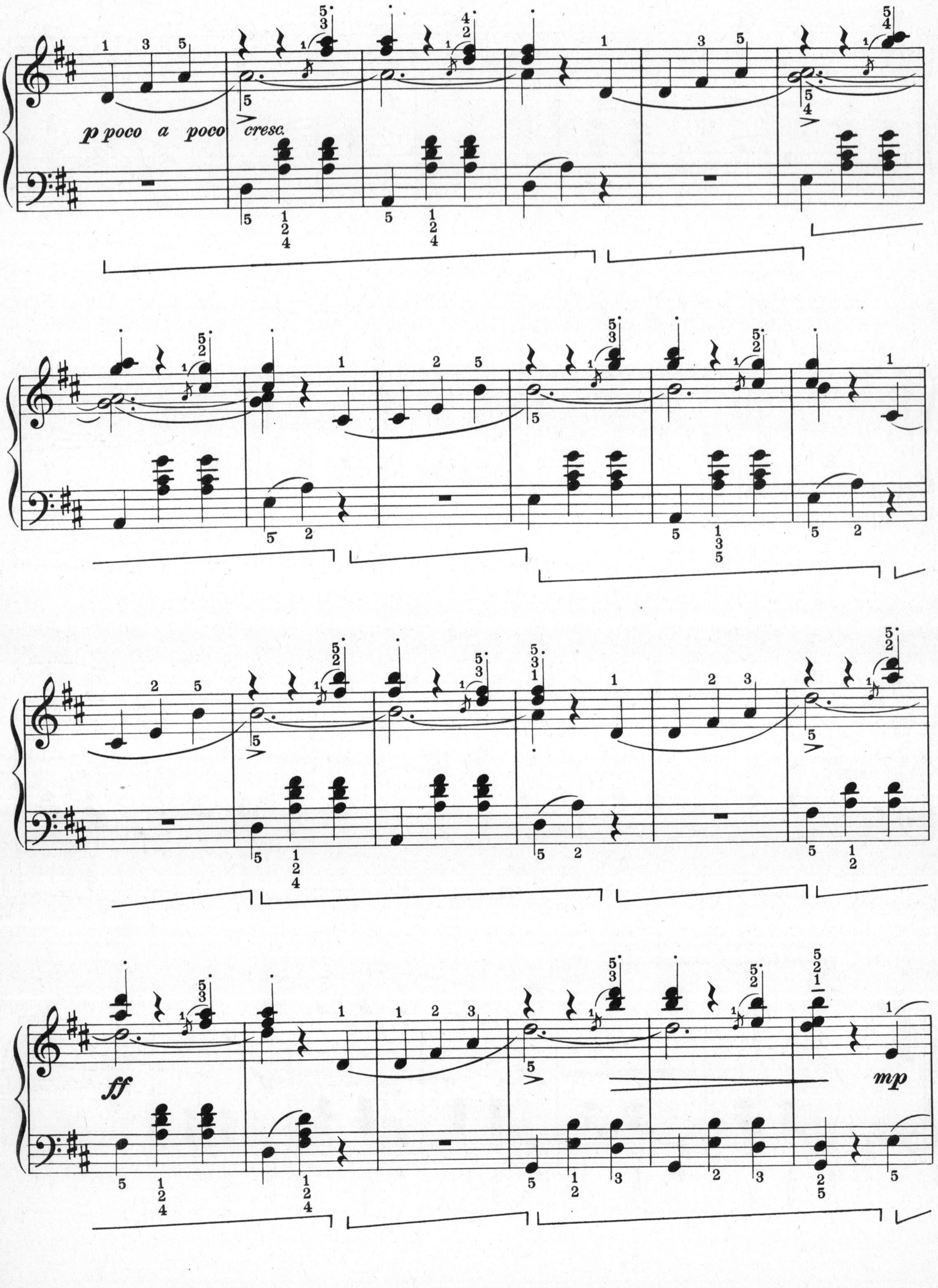
p poco a poco cresc.
ff
mp

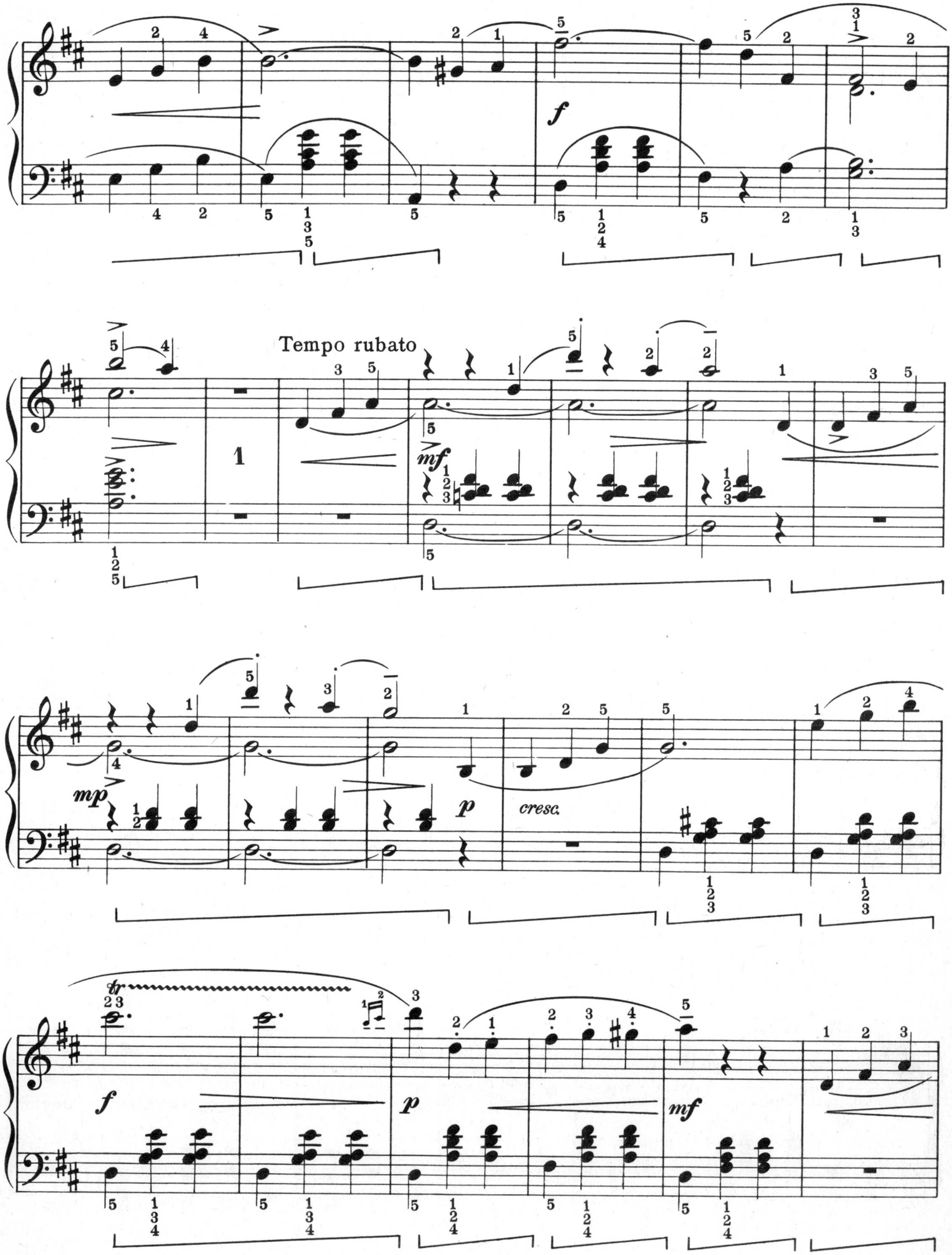
Tempo rubato
cresc.

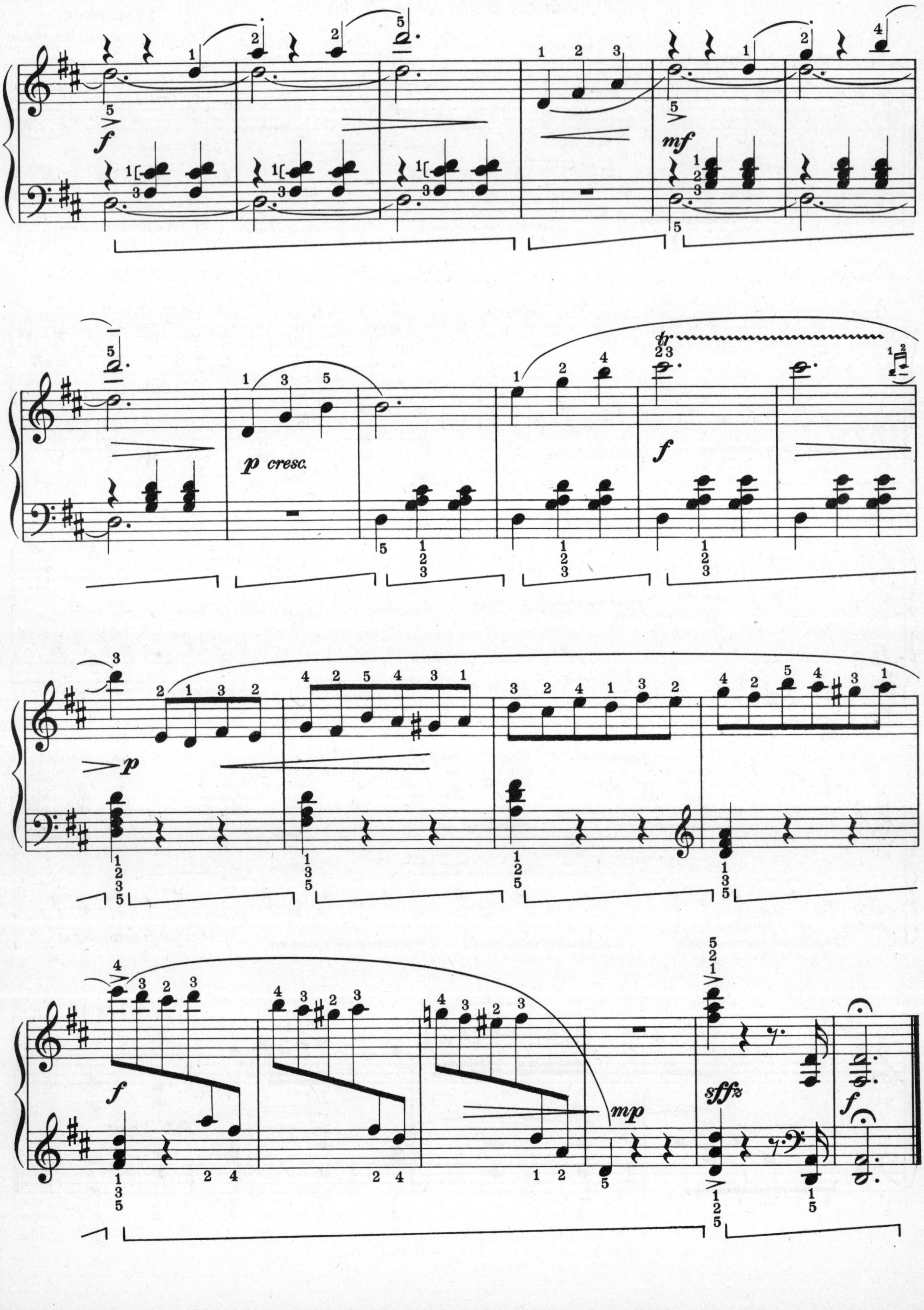
f
mf
p cresc.
tr
f
p
f
mp
sffz
f

MINUET

(From the Sonata, Op. 49, № 2)

Beethoven
Arr. by Bernard Wagness

Tempo di Menuetto

With a broadly arched hand and firmly cushioned fingers, caress the keys with a deep touch aided by a heavy but springy elastic arm and wrist, rotating from key to key. Draw a rich, floating melody tone out of the piano, large enough to soar above the prevailing accompaniment. Refer to Figures A and B.

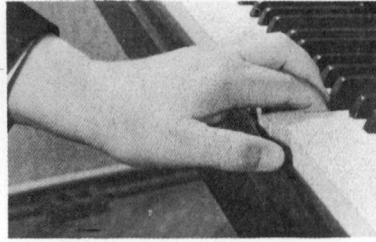

Figure A

Figure B

Franz Liszt was born in Raiding, Hungary, on October 22, 1811. He was a very brilliant pianist and played with the dash and sparkle of a gipsy. After several years of musical study in Vienna, he moved to Paris, where he composed, concertized, and taught for fifteen years.

He was a most generous person and because of his financial successes was able to help many needy friends. In 1849 he established residence in Weimar, Germany, later moving to Rome, where he became an Abbe because of his deep religious feeling. He died in 1886.

LIEBESTRAUM
(A DREAM OF LOVE)

Franz Liszt
Arranged by Bernard Wagness

Allegro non tanto

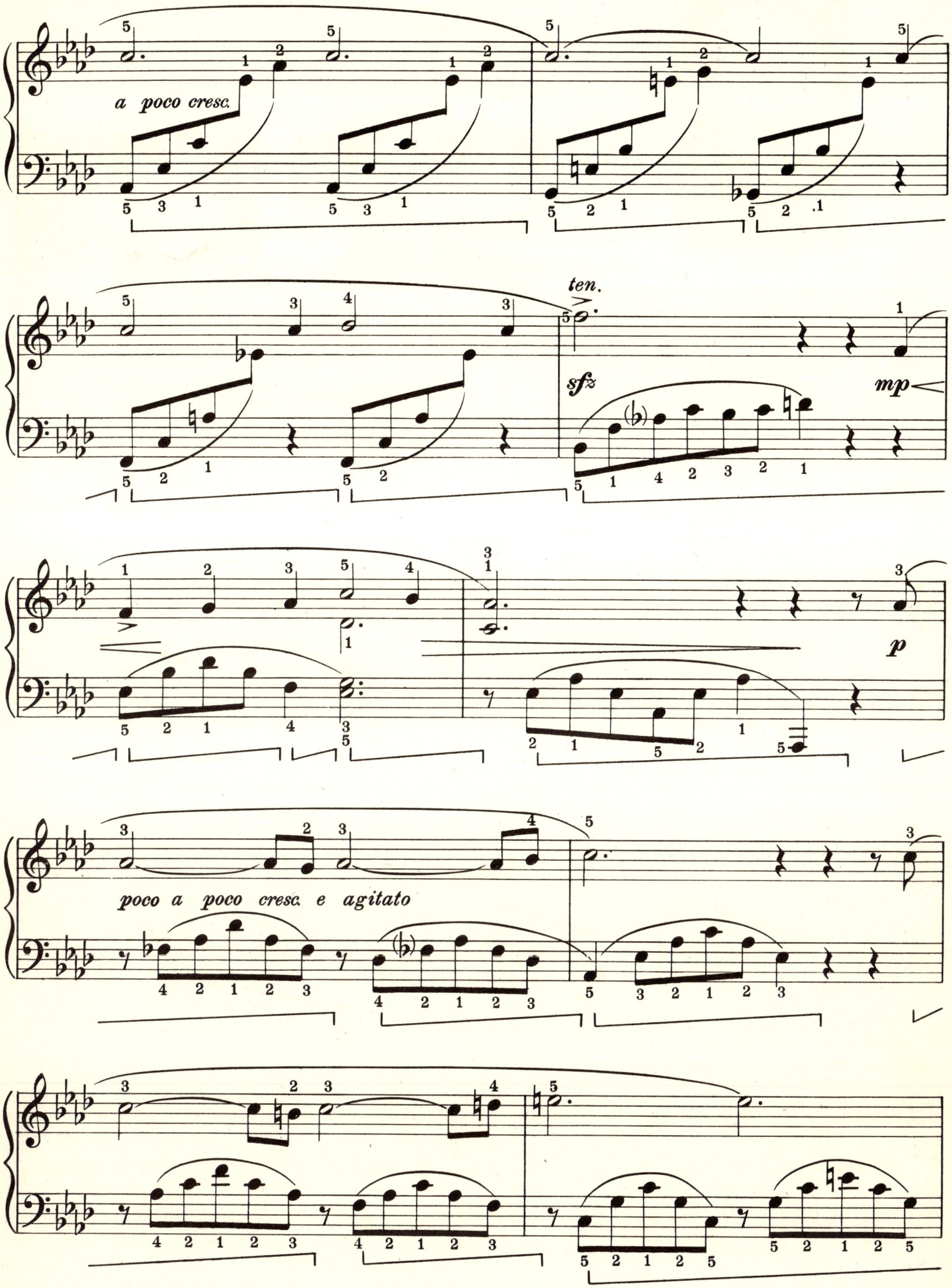
a poco cresc.
ten.
sfz
mp
p
poco a poco cresc. e agitato

sfz
poco ritard.
R.H.
Tempo I
R.H.
L.H.
p teneramente poco a poco cresc.
mf
p
mp

ten.
poco a poco cresc.
sfz
slentando
f
mf
ten.
sfz
espressivo
pp

This prelude is the first number in a collection called "The Well-tempered Clavichord." Bach wrote this collection to prove his new system of tuning the clavichord. Up to the time of Bach, music could be played only in certain keys without retuning the instrument. Bach evolved a scientific system of tonal units whereby each octave was divided into twelve units and one could play in twelve major and twelve minor keys without having to change the tonality of the instrument through tuning. Therefore Johann Sebastian Bach is the father of modern music as we know it today.

In early practice block all broken chord patterns into solid harmonic groups. This piece calls for a firm, clear legato touch and it is to be played in an even, regular tempo. Observe all shading and dynamic markings.

PRELUDE
(№1, from the Well-tempered Clavichord)

Bach

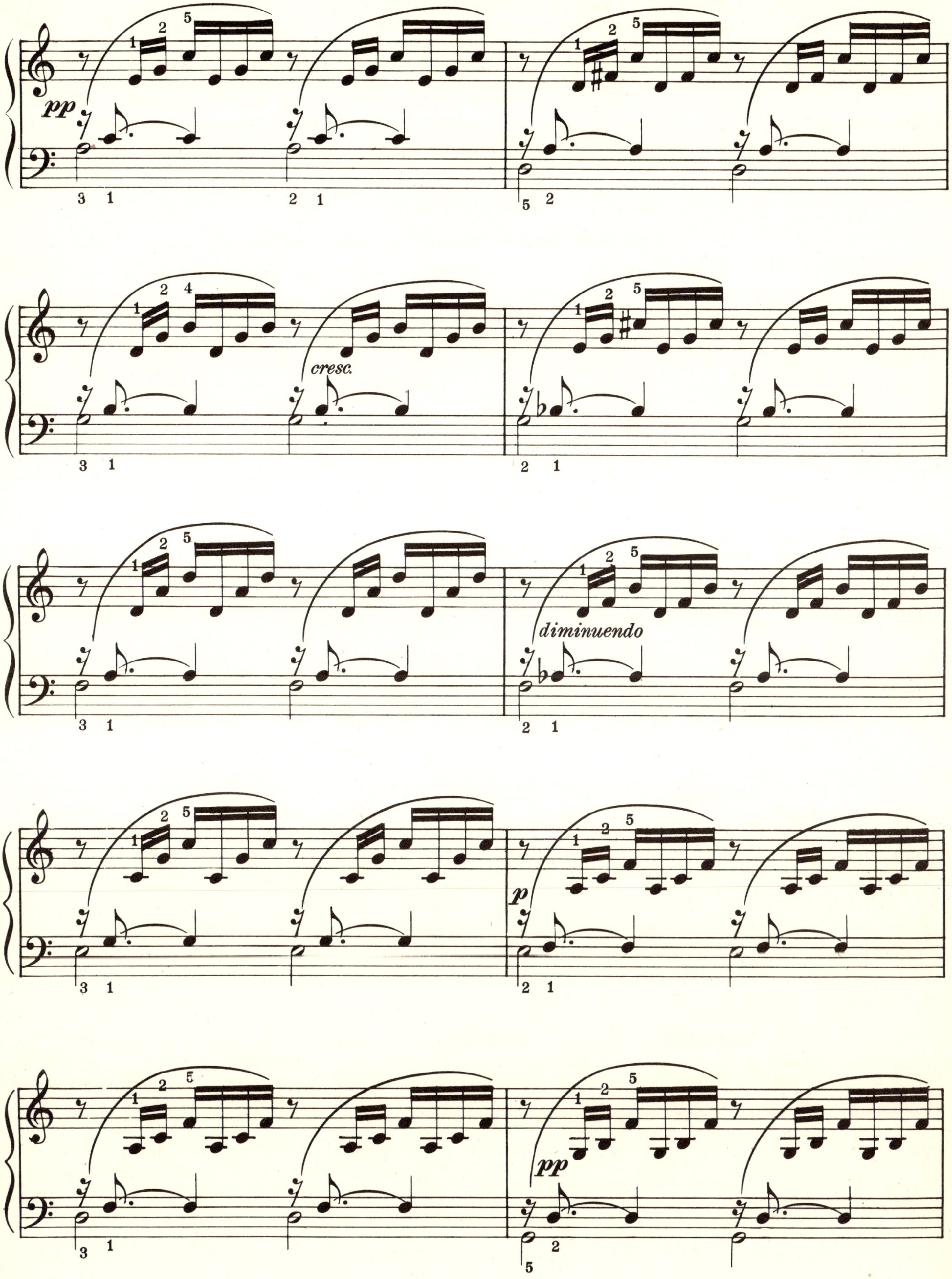
pp
cresc.
diminuendo
p
pp

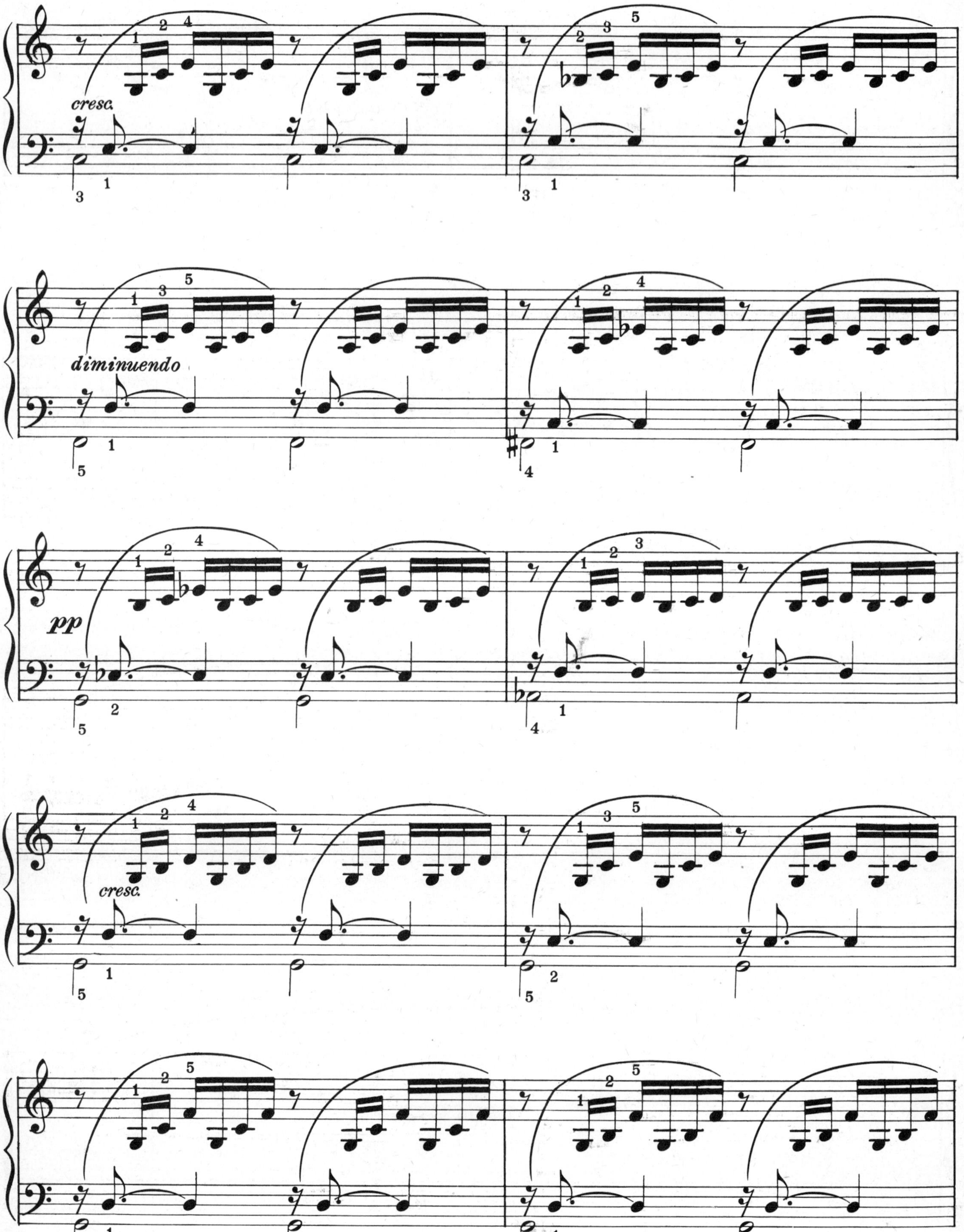
cresc.
diminuendo
pp
cresc.

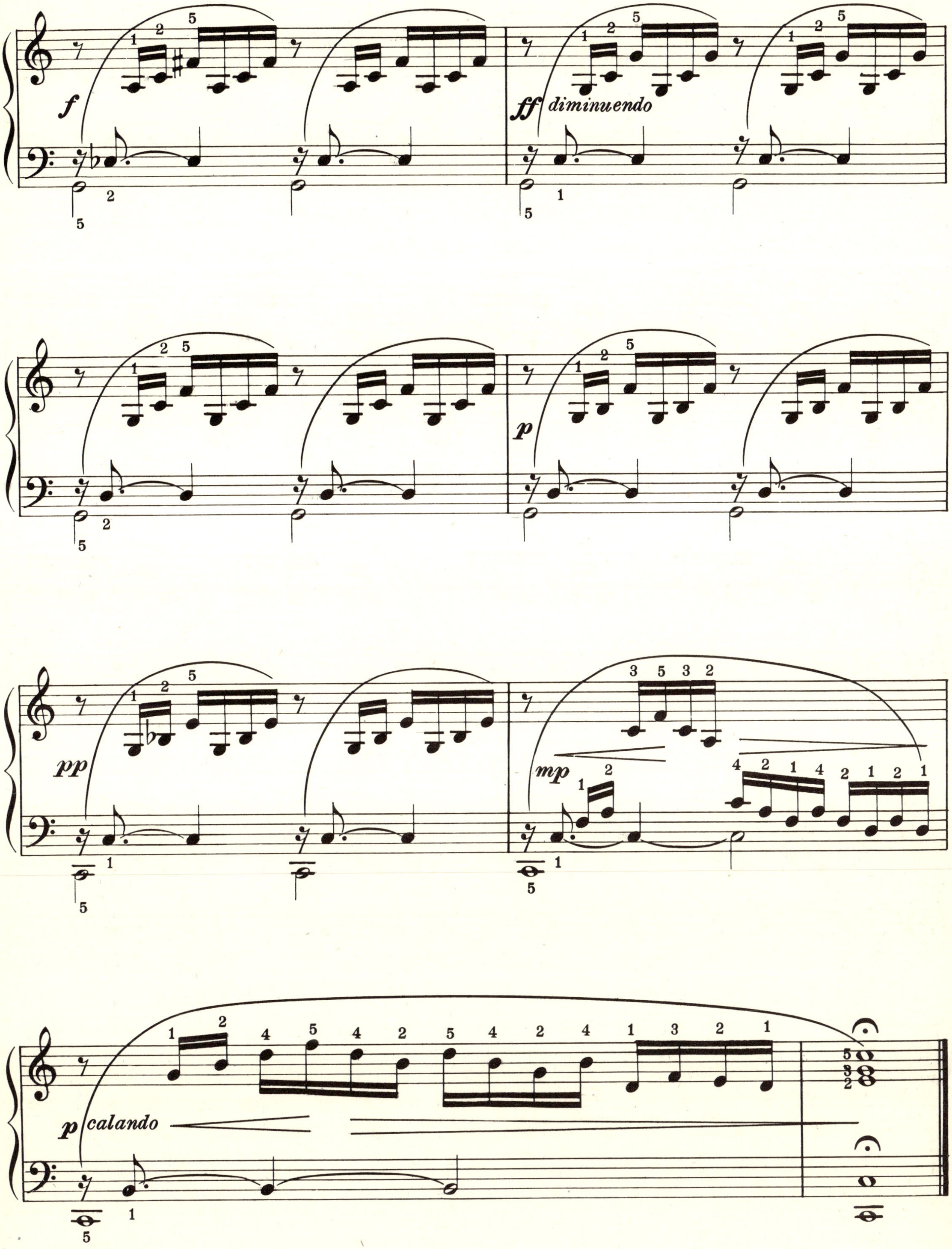
f
ff diminuendo
p
pp
mp
p calando

Giovanni Pierluigi da Palestrina was born
in 1525 and died in 1594. As a young boy
he joined the church choir, later playing the
organ. After establishing residence in Rome,
Palestrina gave up his life to composing music
for the church and to elevating the standards
of church music to the highest degree. His
compositions are divine, lofty and inspiring.

GLORIA PATRI

Palestrina
Harmonized by Bernard Wagness

mp dolce
p leggiero
p sost.
f
più moto
p
mp
ten.
ten.
f in a broad style

The Courante (Italian) and the Corrente (French) is a dance that springs from these two countries. It is a lively, graceful dance performed with short quick running steps in triple time.

Because of the contrapuntal character of classical music, the pianist should make the most of all legato, staccato, accent, dynamic and shading markings. Ignoring these important essentials in expression causes this form of music to be of little interest or meaning.

COURANTE IN G MAJOR

Handel

Allegro

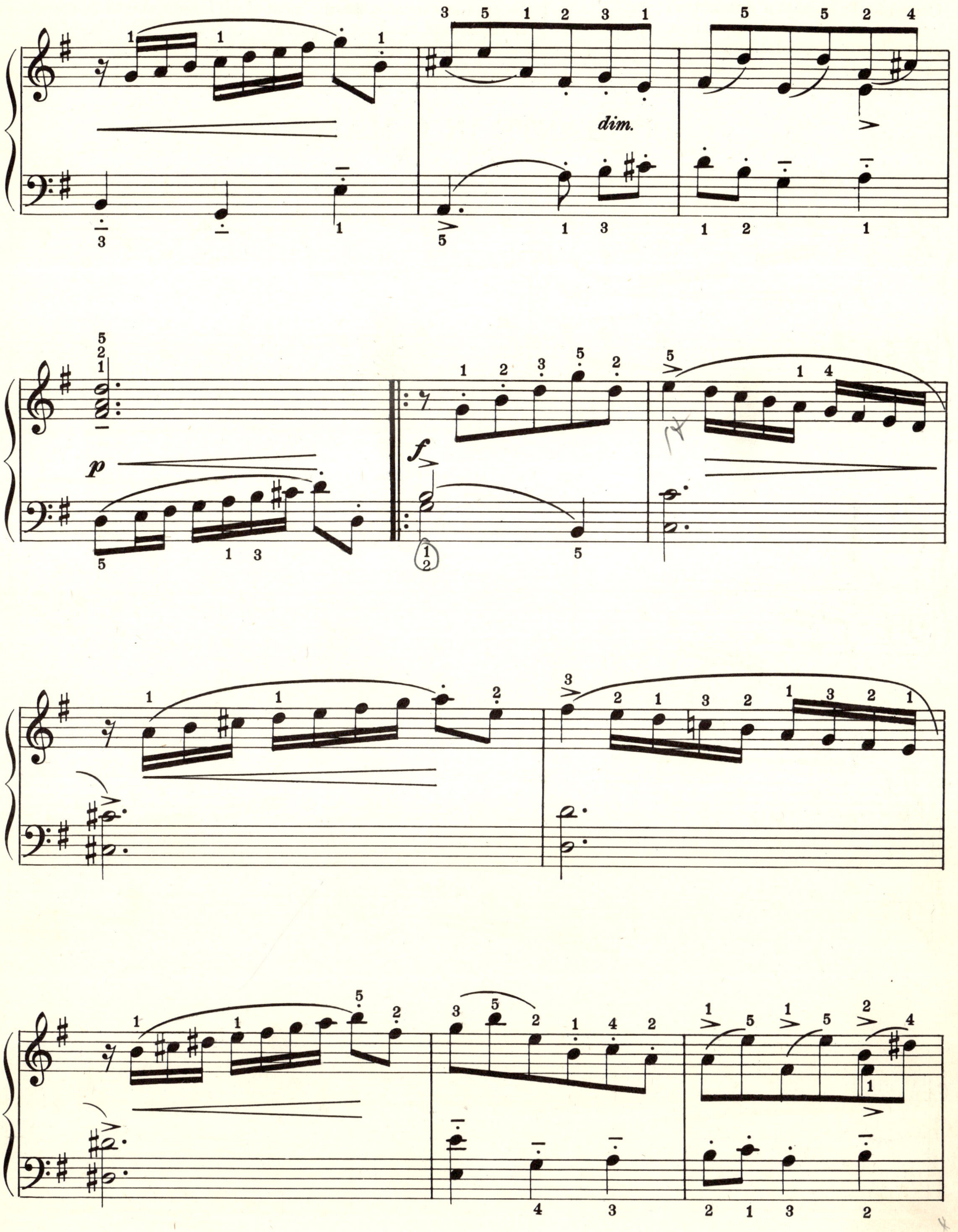
dim.
p
f

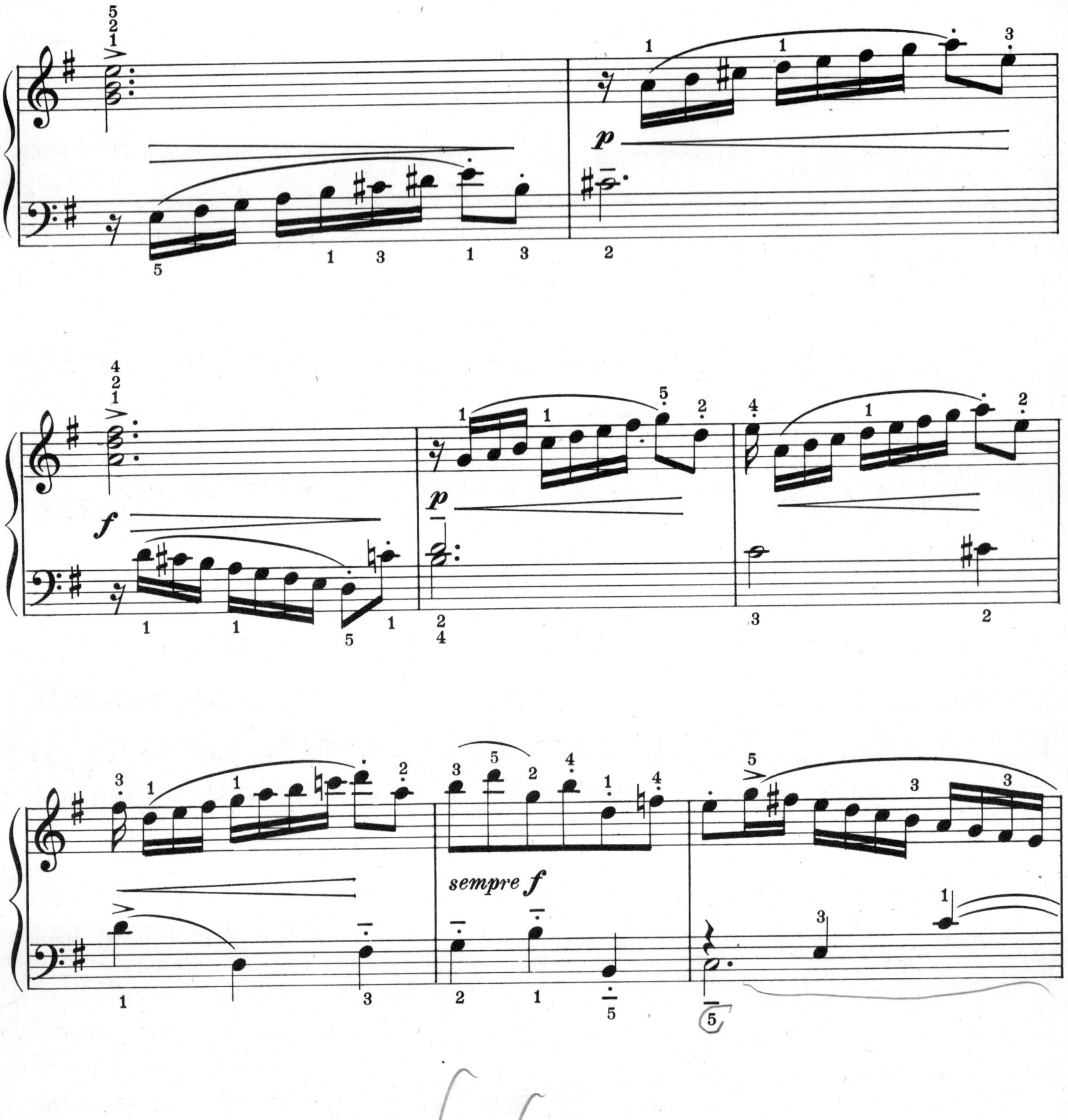
sempre f

WINDMILLS

Hanon

With a broadly arched right hand caress the keys in a rotary upward and outward swinging motion, moving in one continuous circle from the position as illustrated in Figure A to the next position as shown in Figure B. These two levels form an oval circle, causing the arm weight to be pivoted and balanced from key to key, meanwhile forcing the fingers to support this arm weight, thus producing a deep, rich, resonant melody tone.

In the left hand accompaniment patterns sound the keys by means of small, gentle wrist dips, catching each repeated key on the rebound, thus preserving the necessary legato effect. In order to preserve balance and suppleness in the arm, employ an alternating level to high wrist position for each new group, as designated.

As control is established, these alternating level-high wrist vibrations must be reduced until they are scarcely noticeable.

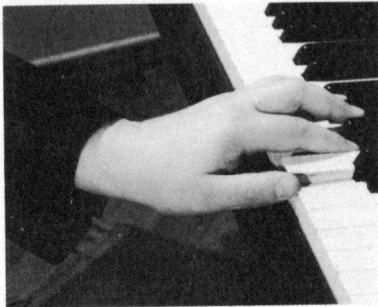

Figure A

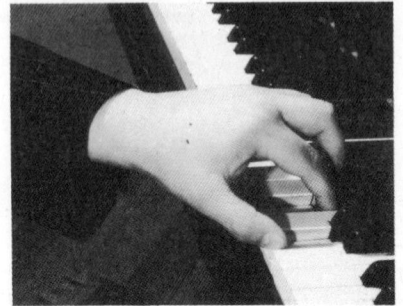

Figure B

INDIAN LEGEND

Andante cantabile

Bernard Wagness

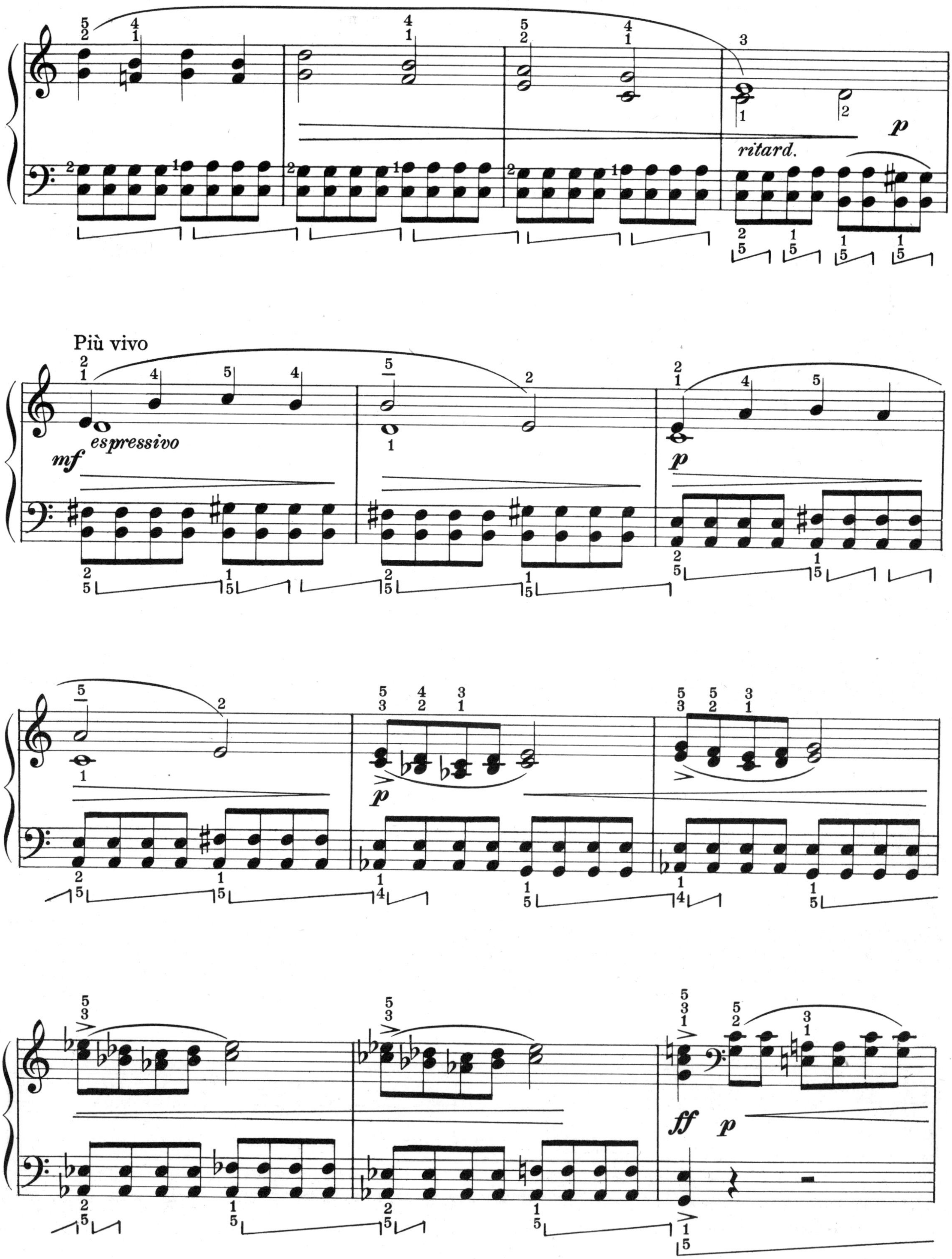
ritard.
Più vivo
espressivo
mf
p
ff

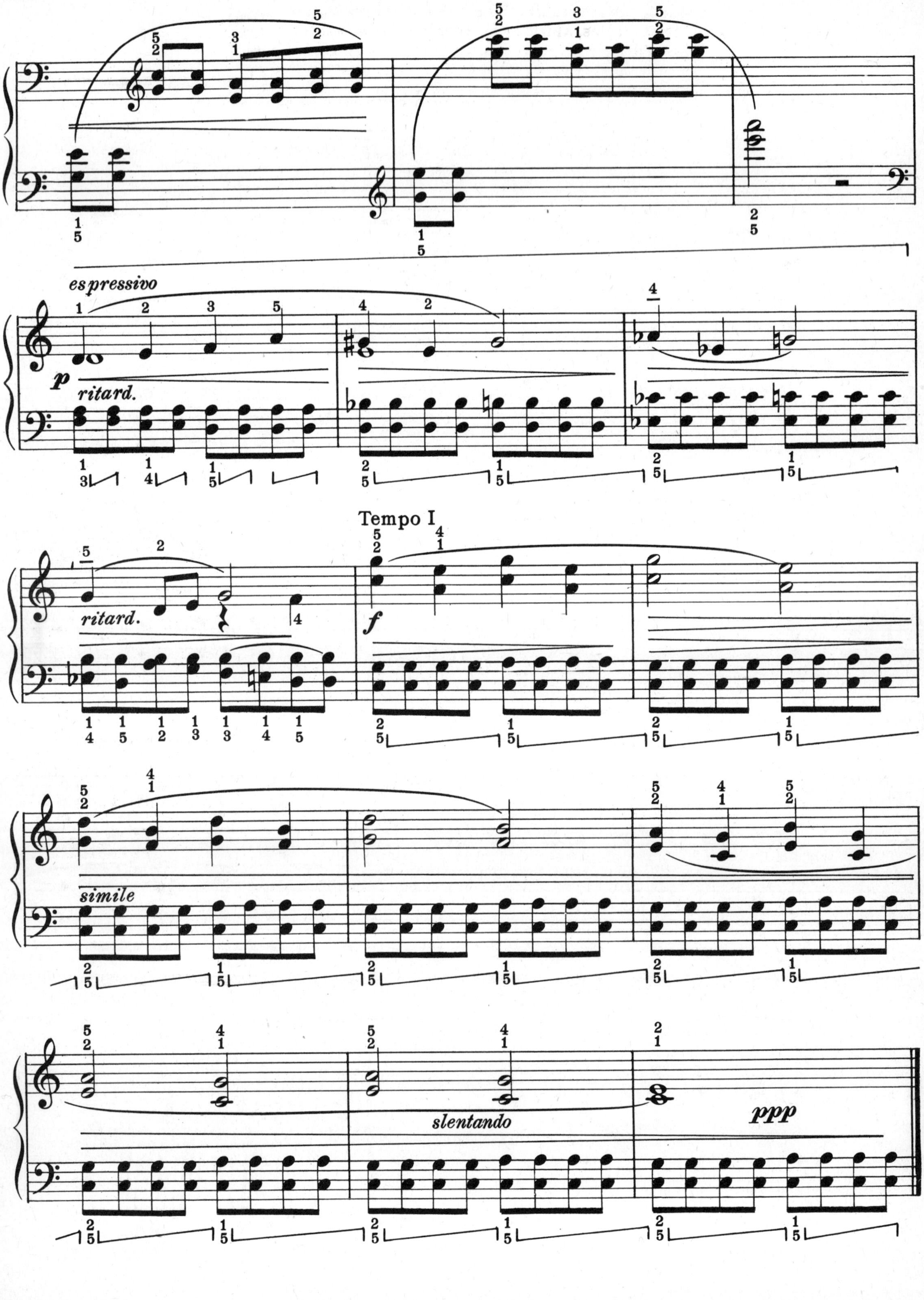
espressivo
ritard.
Tempo I
ritard.
simile
slentando

This Prelude offers pianists a splendid experience in legato chord technic. Employ small, heavy legato chord wrist circles, aided by an undulating arm, working from the shoulder for tone. Gradually reduce the arm pressure, as the tonal demands decrease until suspended arm weight is introduced for the pianissimo section.

PRELUDE IN C MINOR
Op. 28, № 20

Chopin

CONSOLATION

Mendelssohn

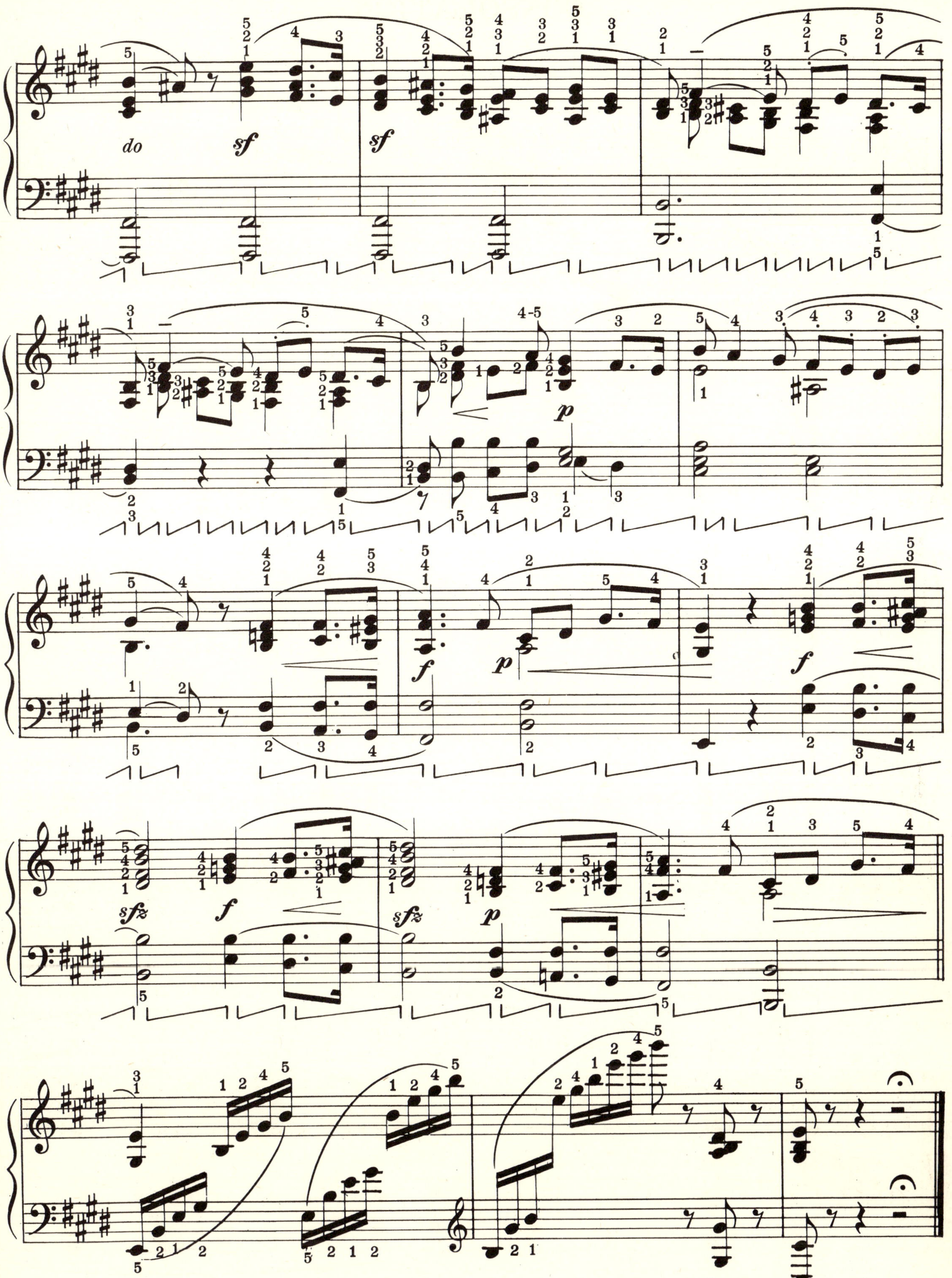
do

The Concerto is a piece consisting of three movements or parts, where some one instrument, generally the piano, violin, or cello, is regarded as the solo instrument and is accompanied by a large or small orchestra. This orchestral accompaniment is also arranged for a second piano. Therefore many piano concertos are really two piano ensembles. Mozart wrote twenty-five concertos. To play Mozart well is a sign of a really fine pianist.

Wolfgang Amadeus Mozart was born at Salzburg, Austria, January 27, 1756. As a little boy Mozart won the hearts of all who heard him play. He appeared in public before he was six years old. At the age of six he had composed pieces for the harpsichord. Mozart lived in Vienna where he composed operas, twenty-five piano concertos and many sonatas for the piano, violin, and organ. He died a pauper in 1791.

ROMANCE
(From the Piano Concerto in D minor)

Mozart

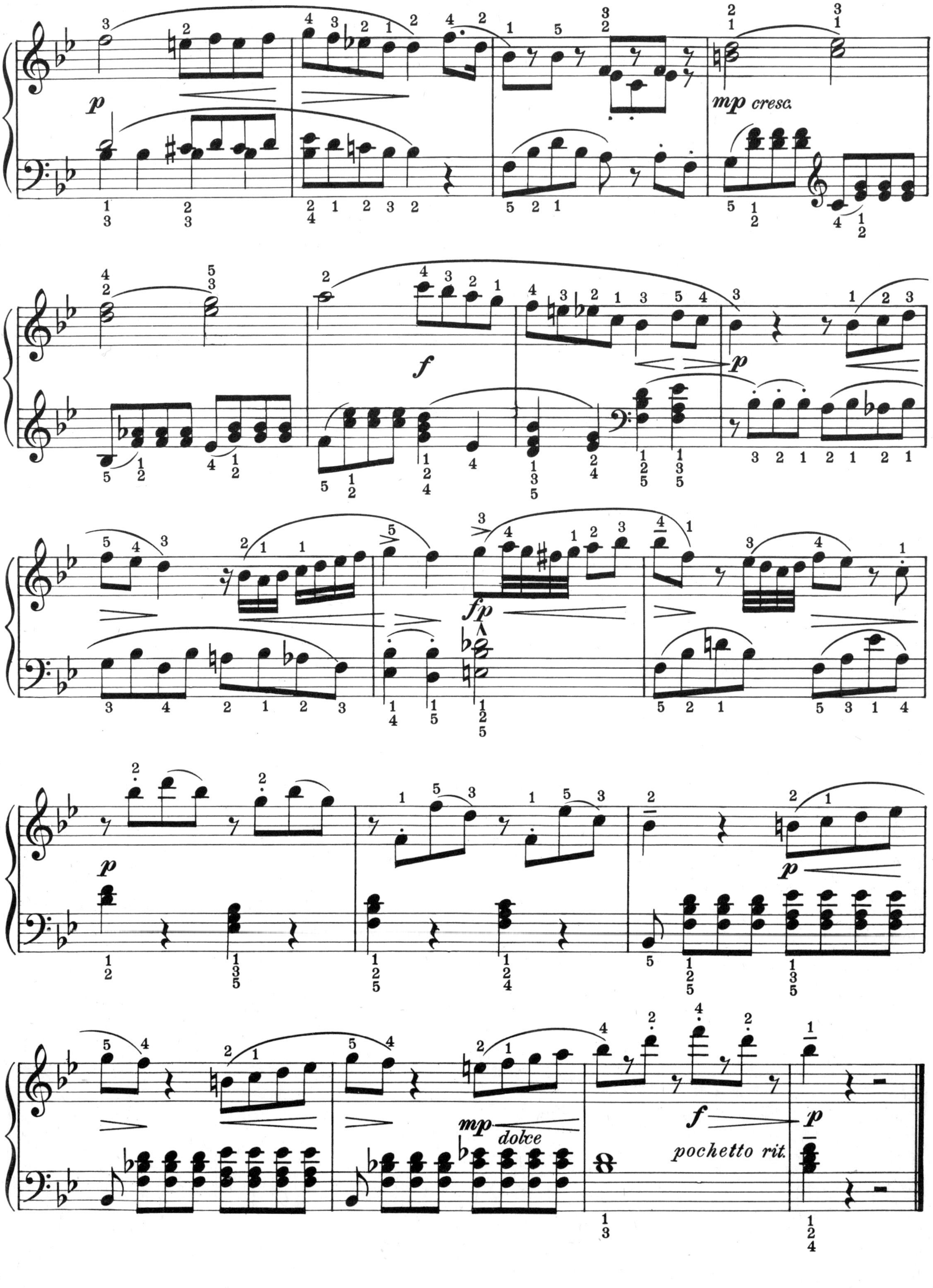
p
mp cresc.
f
p
fp
p
p
mp
dolce
f
pochetto rit.
p

Ludwig van Beethoven was born in Bonn, Germany, December 17, 1770. His parents were very poor. His father was a stern man and would beat Ludwig if he failed to practice each day. At the age of seventeen he visited Vienna where Mozart heard him play. Mozart was very much impressed with Beethoven's ability. He wrote one opera, Fidelio, many symphonies, sonatas and concerti. In his later years Beethoven became very deaf. This affliction affected his health. He died in 1827.

ALBUM LEAF
(Für Elise)

Ludwig van Beethoven

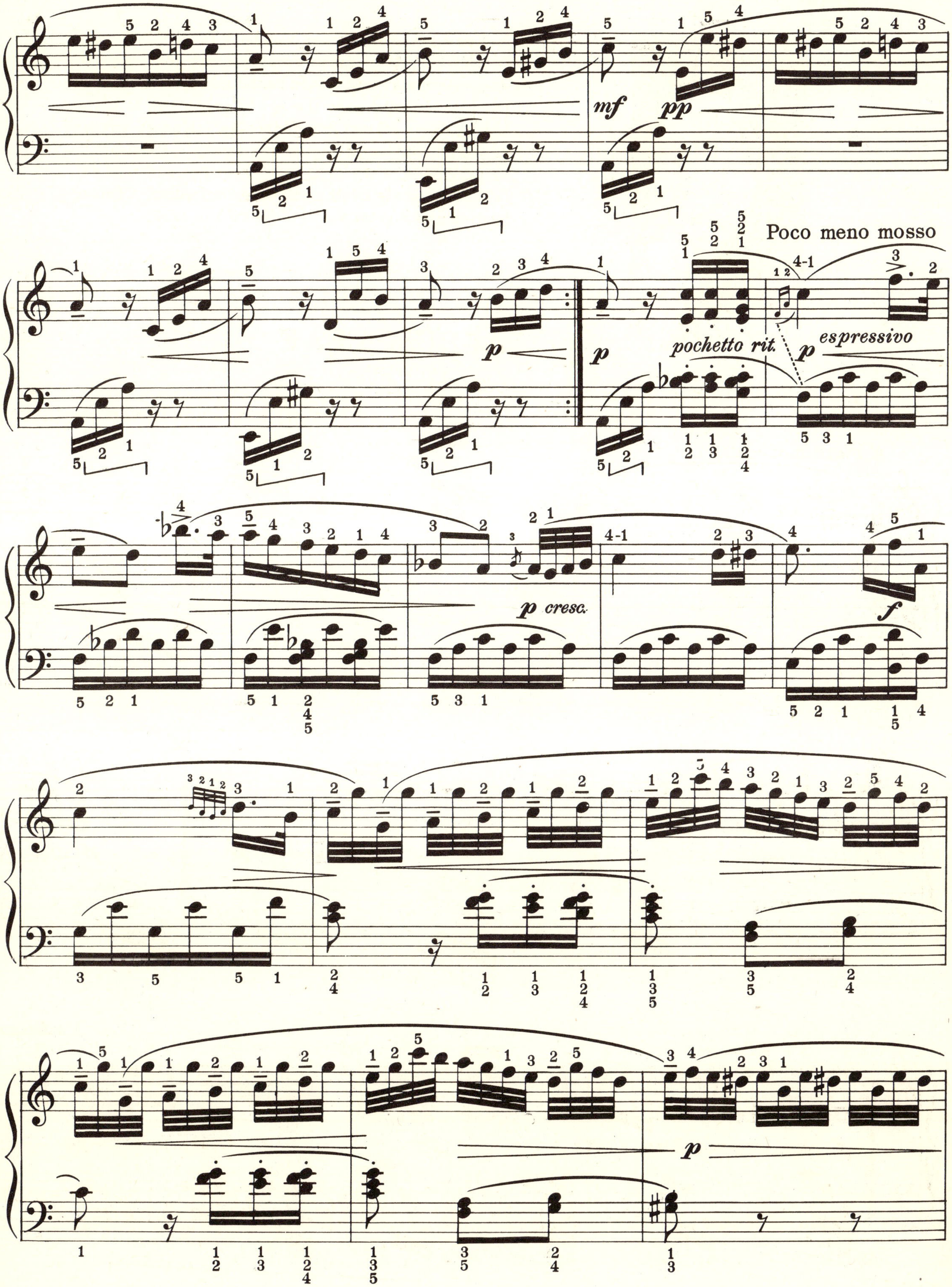
mf
pp
p
Poco meno mosso
pochetto rit.
espressivo
p cresc.
f

Tempo I
pp
pochetto ritard.
pp
mf
pp
p
p
mf
p
pochetto ritard.
a tempo
pp
mf
p cresc.

sfz
sfz
f poco a poco dim.
Ped. simile
ten.
p cresc.
Ped. simile
ten.
ff poco a poco dim.
pp leggiero
8
pochetto ritard.

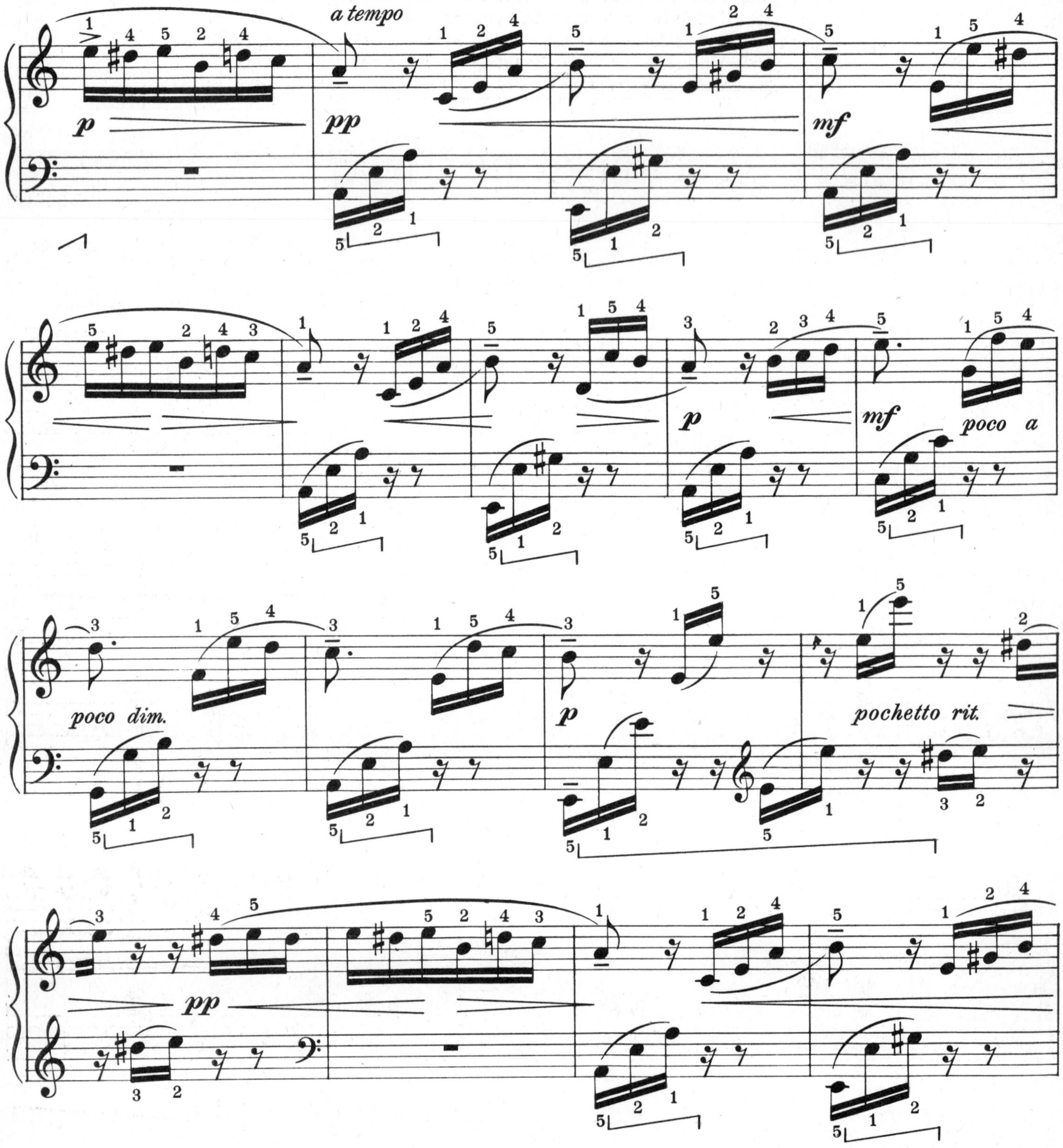
a tempo
p
pp
mf
p
mf
poco a
poco dim.
p
pochetto rit.
pp
pp
p
ten.
ten.

Through careful pedaling of this Scherzo, the player will be
greatly aided in in avoiding a thin tone and a dry interpretation.
The staccato patterns in the right hand section must be carefully
executed; the pedal, however, must be used to tie together these
various harmonic patterns. Do not play this number too rapidly.

SCHERZO IN B FLAT

Schubert

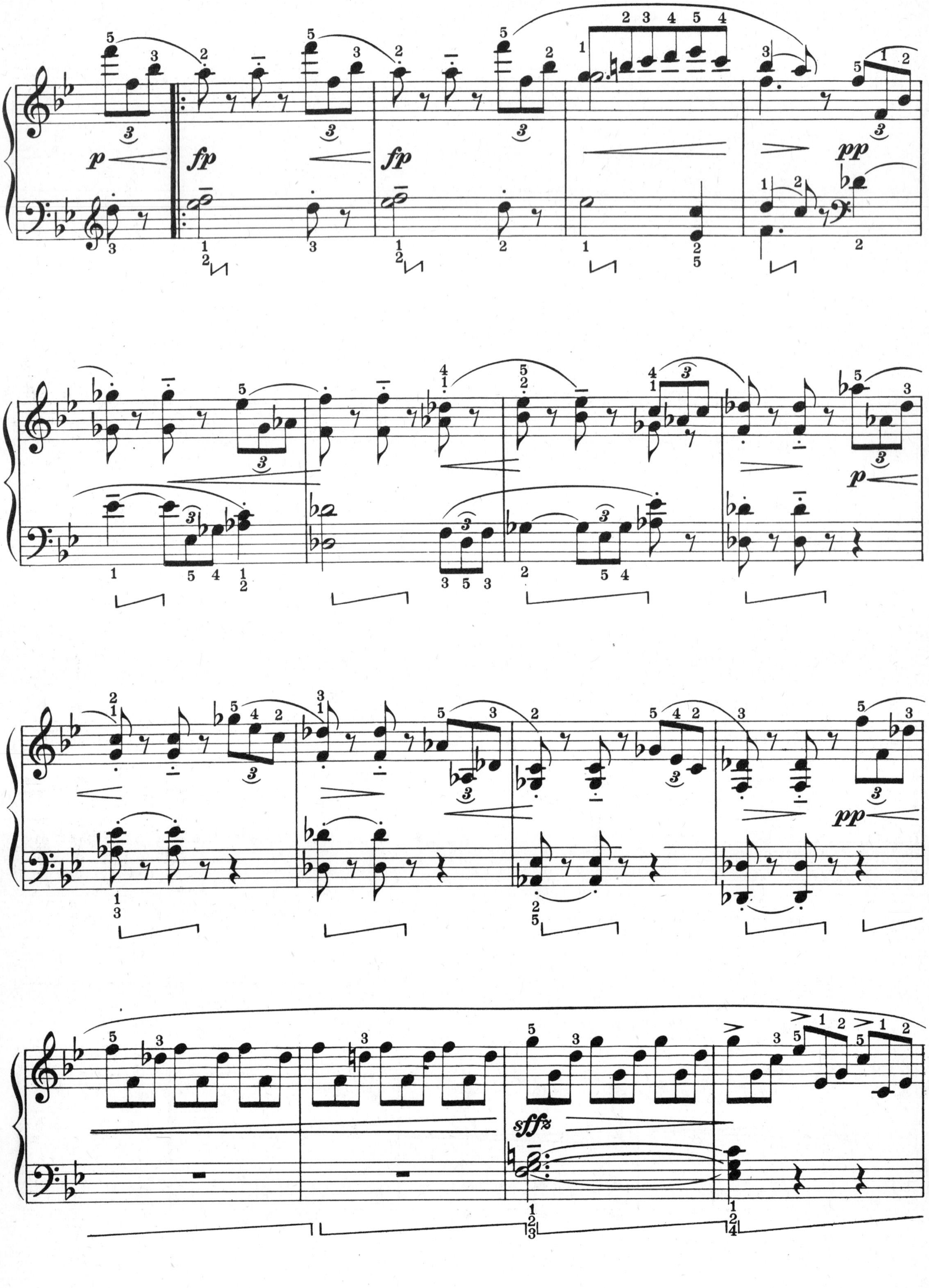
p
fp
fp
pp
p
pp
sffz

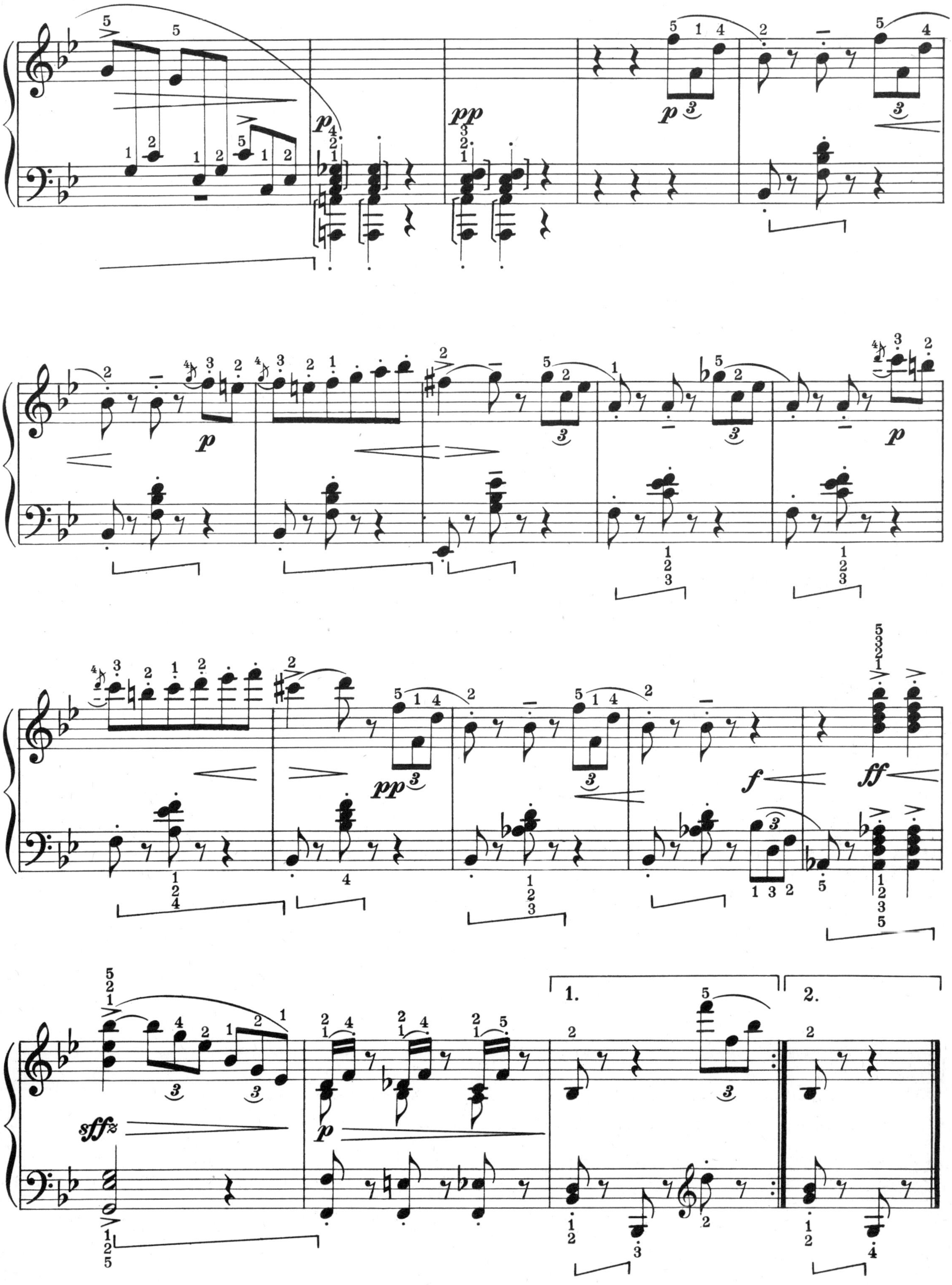

Gregorio Turini was born at Brescia, Italy, about 1540. This Italian musician was attached to the courts of Emperor Maximilian II and Rudolf II at Prague. He was a composer, singer and cornetist, his compositions consisting of sacred and secular vocal music. He died at Prague about 1600.

HODIE CHRISTUS NATUS EST

Gregorio Turini (1540-1600)
Harmonized by Bernard Wagness

animato
ff
p cresc.
sfz
mf
mp
p
p largamente e cresc. Sin 'al fine
sffz

This composition is one of a group called "The Little Preludes", a collection of pieces written by Bach for one of his sons, who was studying with his father.

PRELUDE IN F MAJOR

Bach

Johann Sebastian Bach was born in 1685 at Eisenach, Germany. He was the most noted of a famous family of outstanding musicians of that day. Bach was a loving father to his twenty children. He was a wonderful performer at the organ and clavichord, as well as being a conductor of choirs in churches. He composed a tremendous amount of the world's finest music. This is most remarkable because he was a pioneer in the modern forms of composition which are today considered monuments in musical literature. He died July 28, 1750.

Practice this Prelude at first hands separately
and in sections, blocking each broken chord pattern
into solid groups. Play with a forte touch, first
staccato and then non-legato. Give as much atten-
tion to the left hand parts as you do to the right
hand parts.

For the right hand melody gently caress the keys with firm fingertips, aided by a springy, balanced wrist and arm as in Figure A.

The rather heavy arm will rotate in small, oval circles up to the shoulder, as it swings the hand from one melody tone to the next. Increase the arm weight by means of a small amount of pressure to produce the desired crescendo effects.

Employ small, clinging legato wrist circles in the left hand accompaniment, connecting the tones well with slight wrist dips and an undulating arm and elbow. Bring out each change in harmony.

Figure A

TROUBLED DREAMS

Bernard Wagness

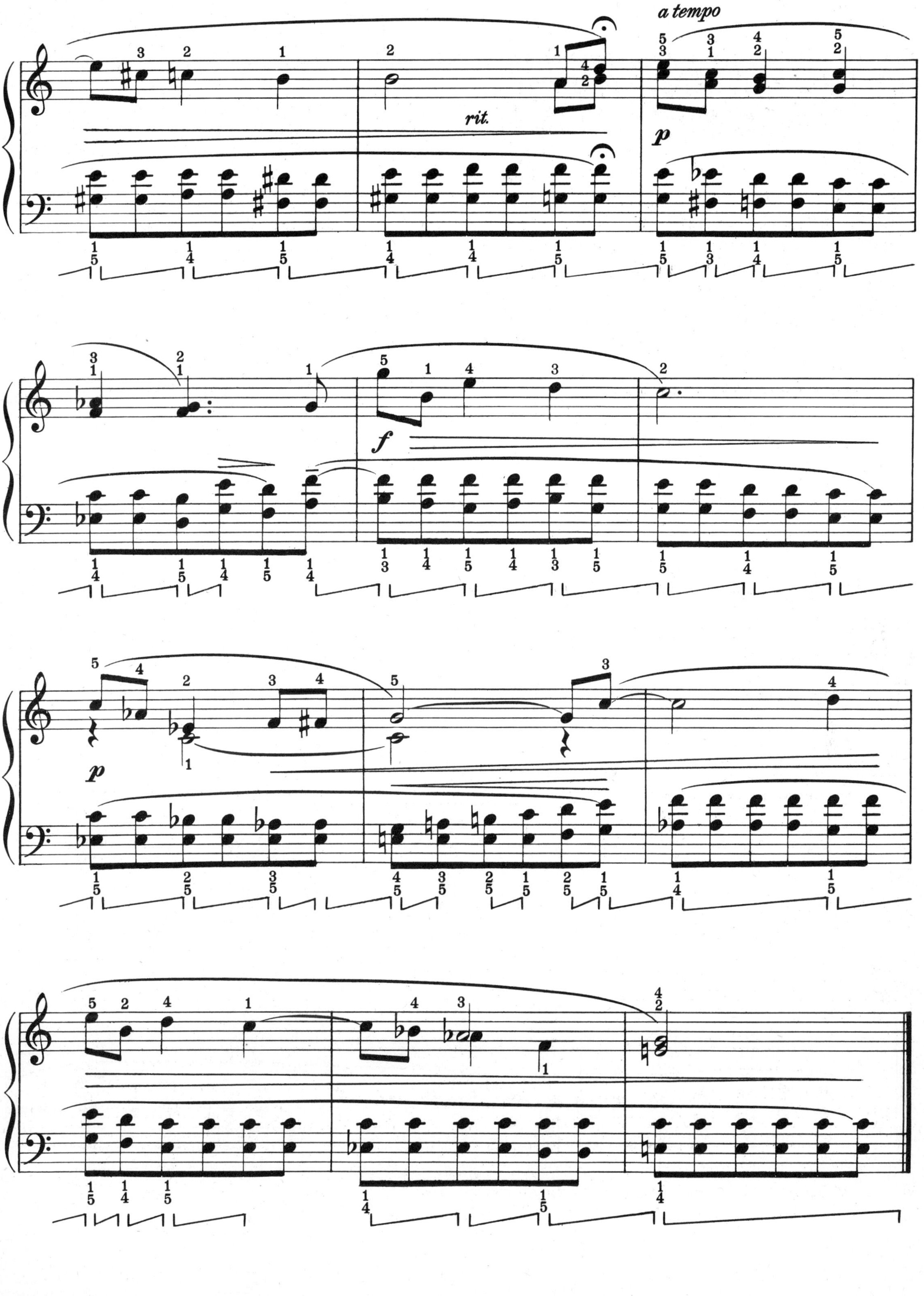
a tempo
rit.

Block all broken chord patterns into solid chord groups during early practice. Play all passage patterns with a non-legato touch at all times, preserving clarity of tone. Give proper emphasis to the left hand, observing the agogic accents and the staccato marks. Use the pedal sparingly.

LITTLE PRELUDE
IN C MINOR

J. S. Bach

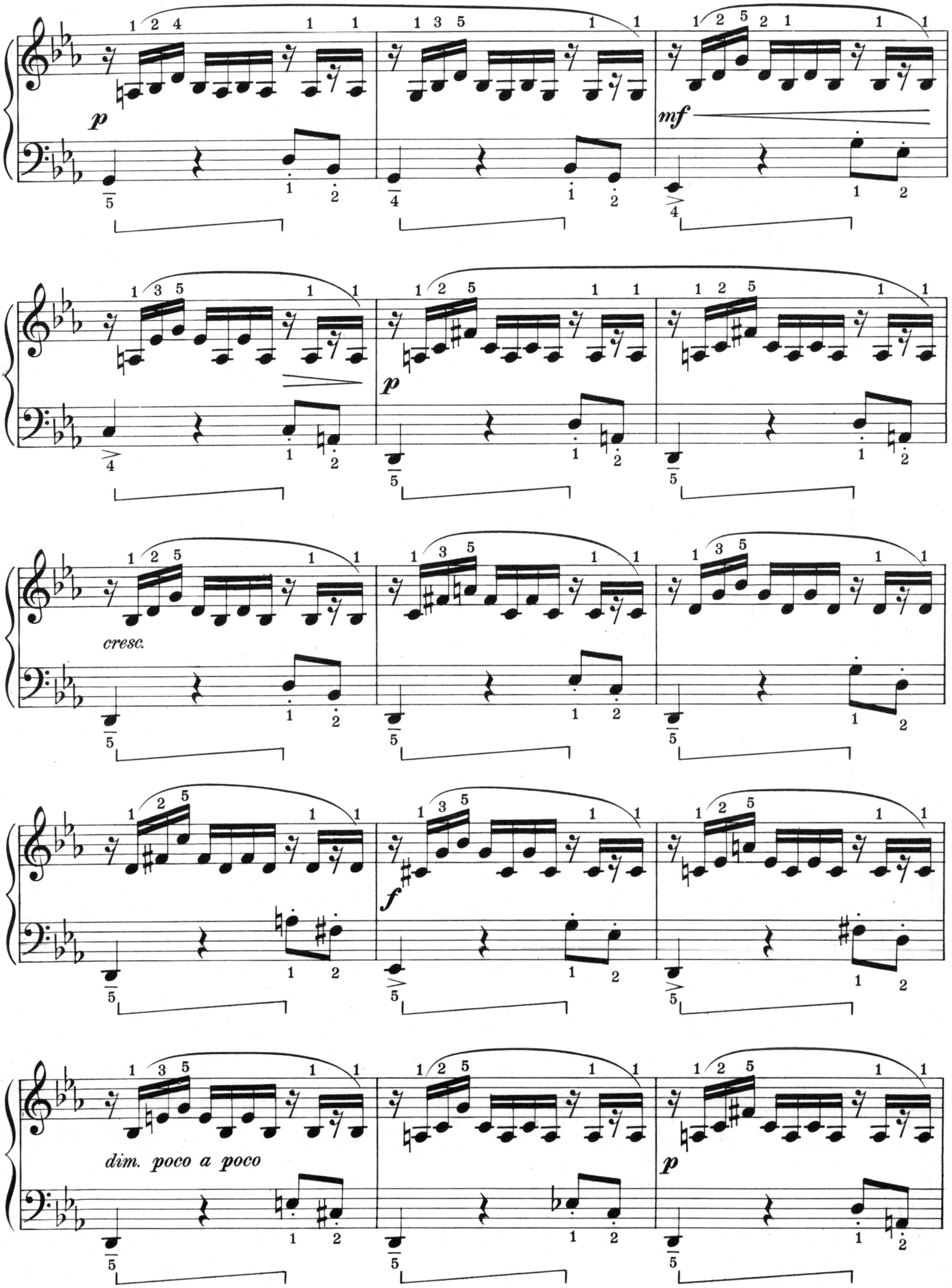
p
mf
p
cresc.
f
dim. poco a poco
p

mf
dim.
p
pp poco rit.
tranquillo
p
mf cresc.
f
p
p
rallentando
dim.
p rall.
mf

Play this Waltz in a smooth flowing style, striving always
for legato, proper shading, and a feeling of moving toward the
goal of each motive which is found in each dotted quarter note.

WALTZ IN A FLAT
Op 39, №15

J. Brahms
Original Phrasing by Bernard Wagness

Tempo giusto ma grazioso

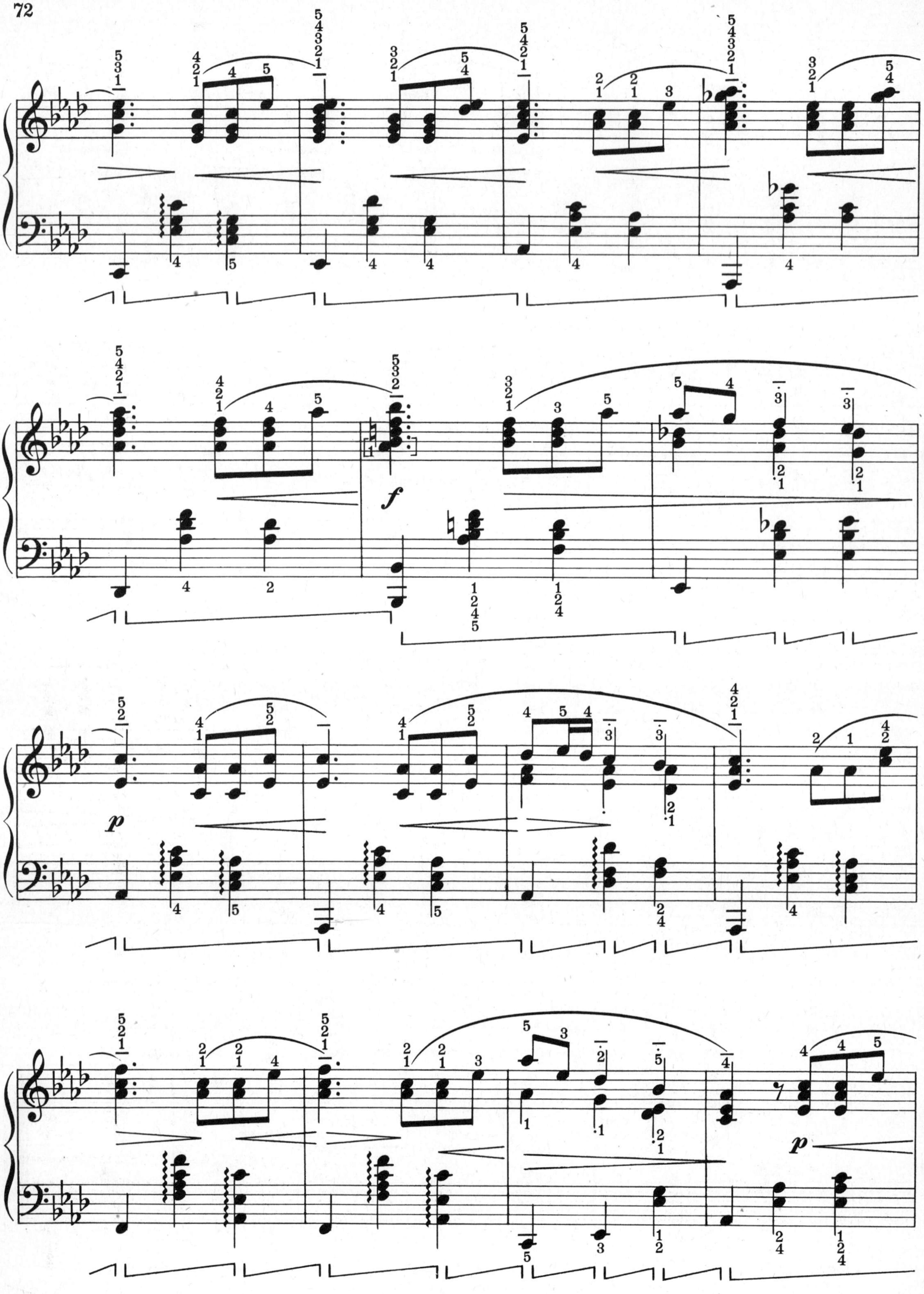

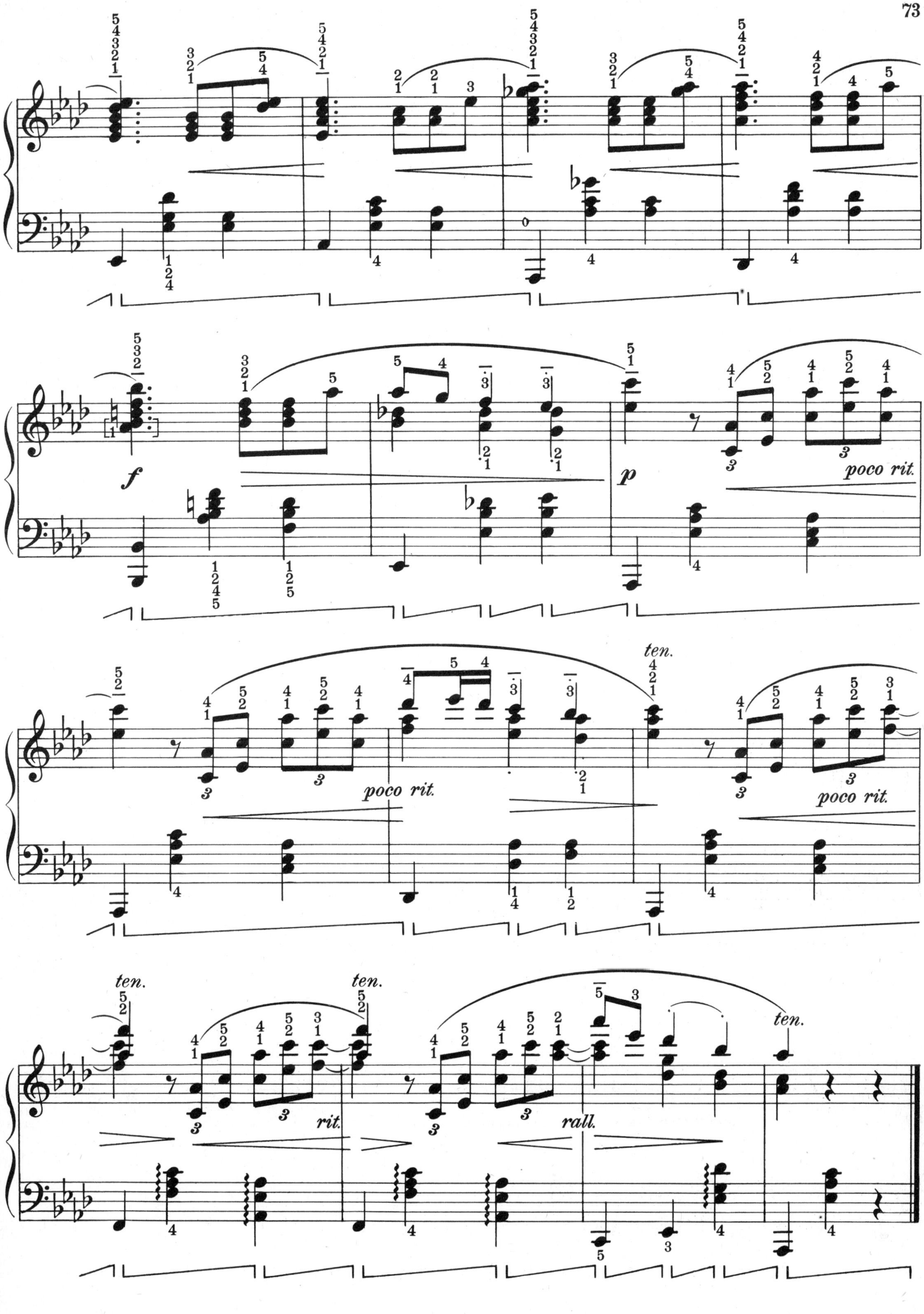
f
p
poco rit.
poco rit.
ten.
poco rit.
ten.
ten.
rit.
rall.
ten.

Figure A

This charming piece contains excellent material for playing themadized sixths where one voice has the melody and the other voice is to be kept in the background a little. As a rule the melody tone in such cases lies in the upper voice. Notice that we are to use the third, fourth and fifth fingers for the upper voice. An aid to improve the legato quality of themadized sixths is recommended.

Directions: Sound the first intervals, as shown below, immediately releasing the thumb tone, thus causing the entire arm weight to be centered in the melody fingertip, as in Figure A.

VALSE CHARMANTE

Bernard Wagness

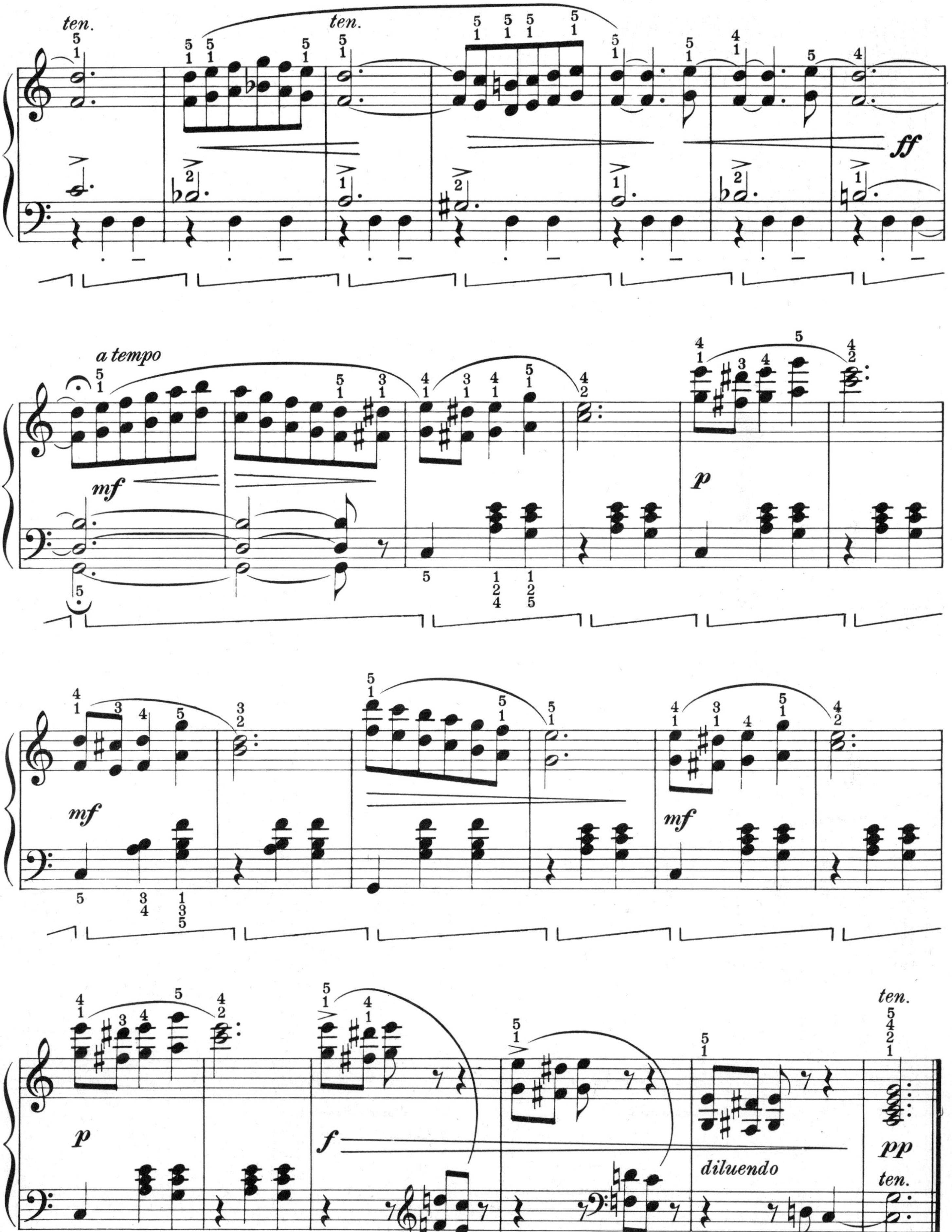
ten.
ten.
ff
a tempo
mf
p
mf
mf
p
f
diluendo
ten.
pp
ten.

This Solfeggietto is one of the most popular of classical compositions. It contains excellent material for developing a classical technic. Employ a positive, well-defined finger touch, with great care given to the speedy lifting of each finger after every key attack. Shade well and bring out all contrasts in dynamics.

Carl Philipp Emanuel Bach was born in March, 1714, at Weimar. He was known as the Berlin or Hamburg Bach, and was the founder of the modern school of piano playing. As a brilliant performer, he was unsurpassed. He composed a great deal of music, and in this way carried out the traditions of his wonderful father, J. S. Bach.

SOLFEGGIETTO

Carl Philipp Emanuel Bach
(1714-1788)

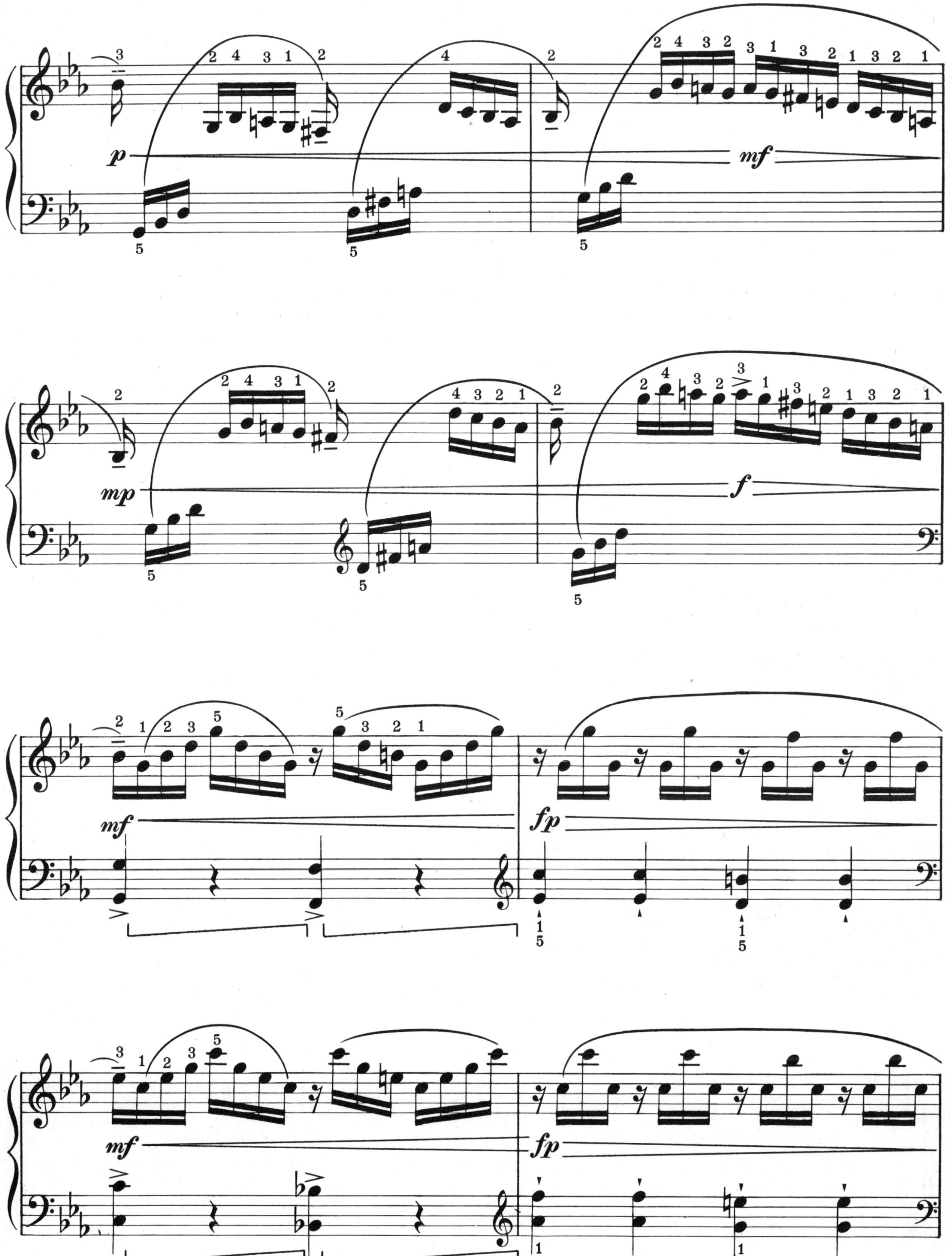
p
mf
mp
f
mf
fp
mf
fp

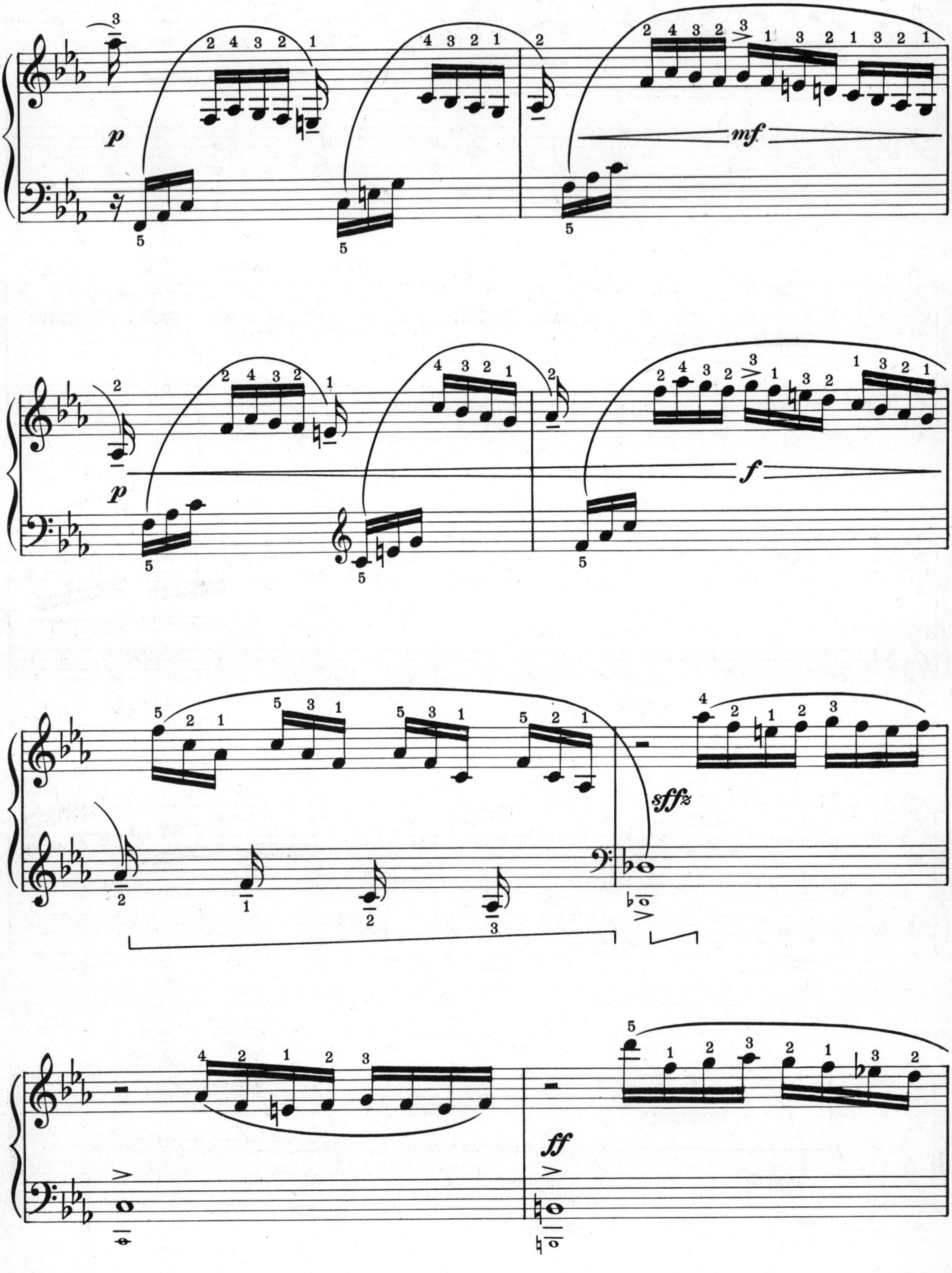
p
mf
p
f
sffz
ff

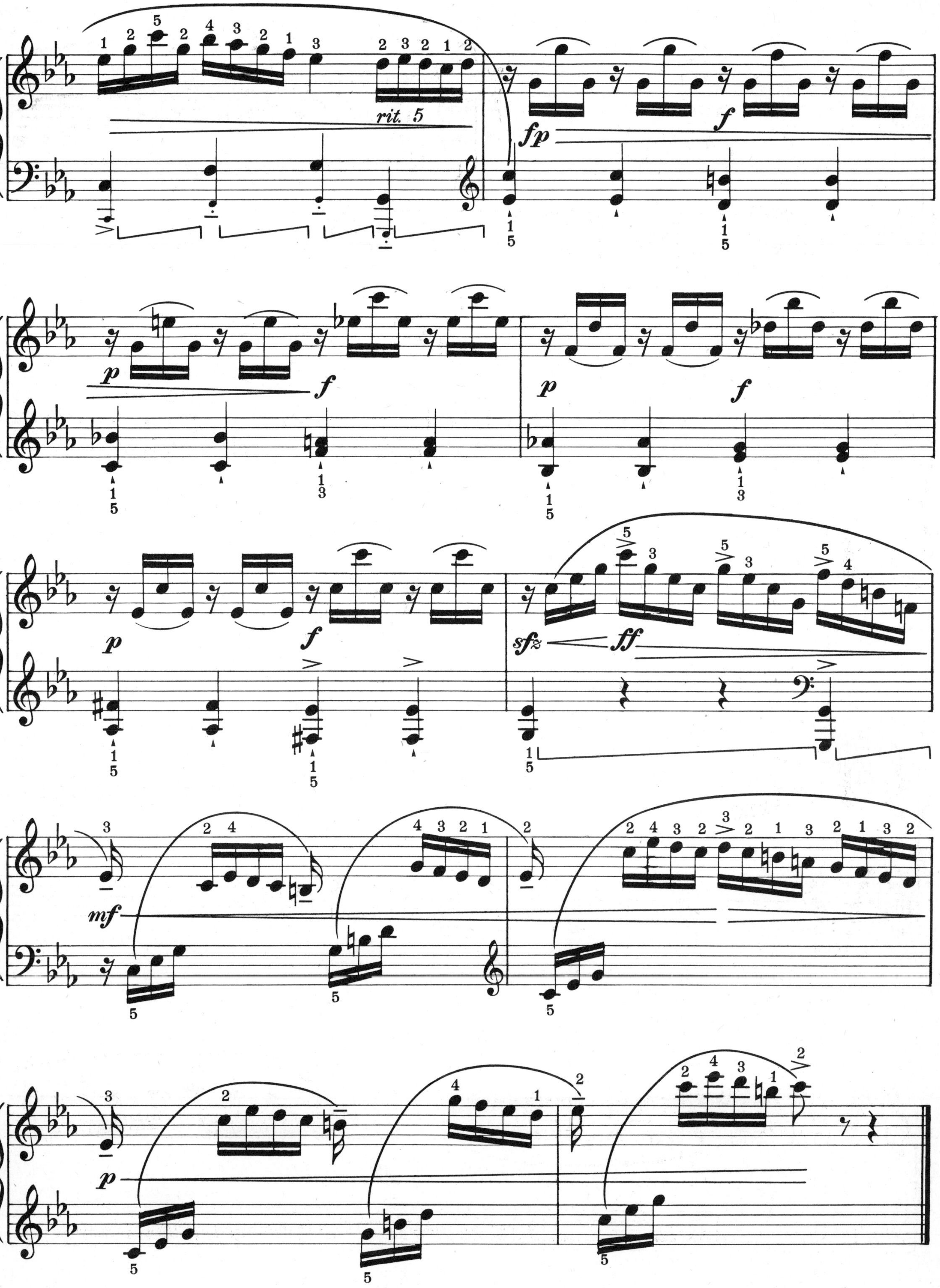
rit.

In this Prelude great care should be taken
to avoid any staleness in the interpretation,
due to the rather limited scope of melody and
accompaniment.   This number is one of the
most beautiful of the Chopin Preludes. In the
melody, strive for constant motion through
shading and rubato.   In the accompaniment,
the left hand must provide a legato background.
Bring out each change in harmony.

PRELUDE IN E MINOR

Chopin
Edited by Bernard Wagness

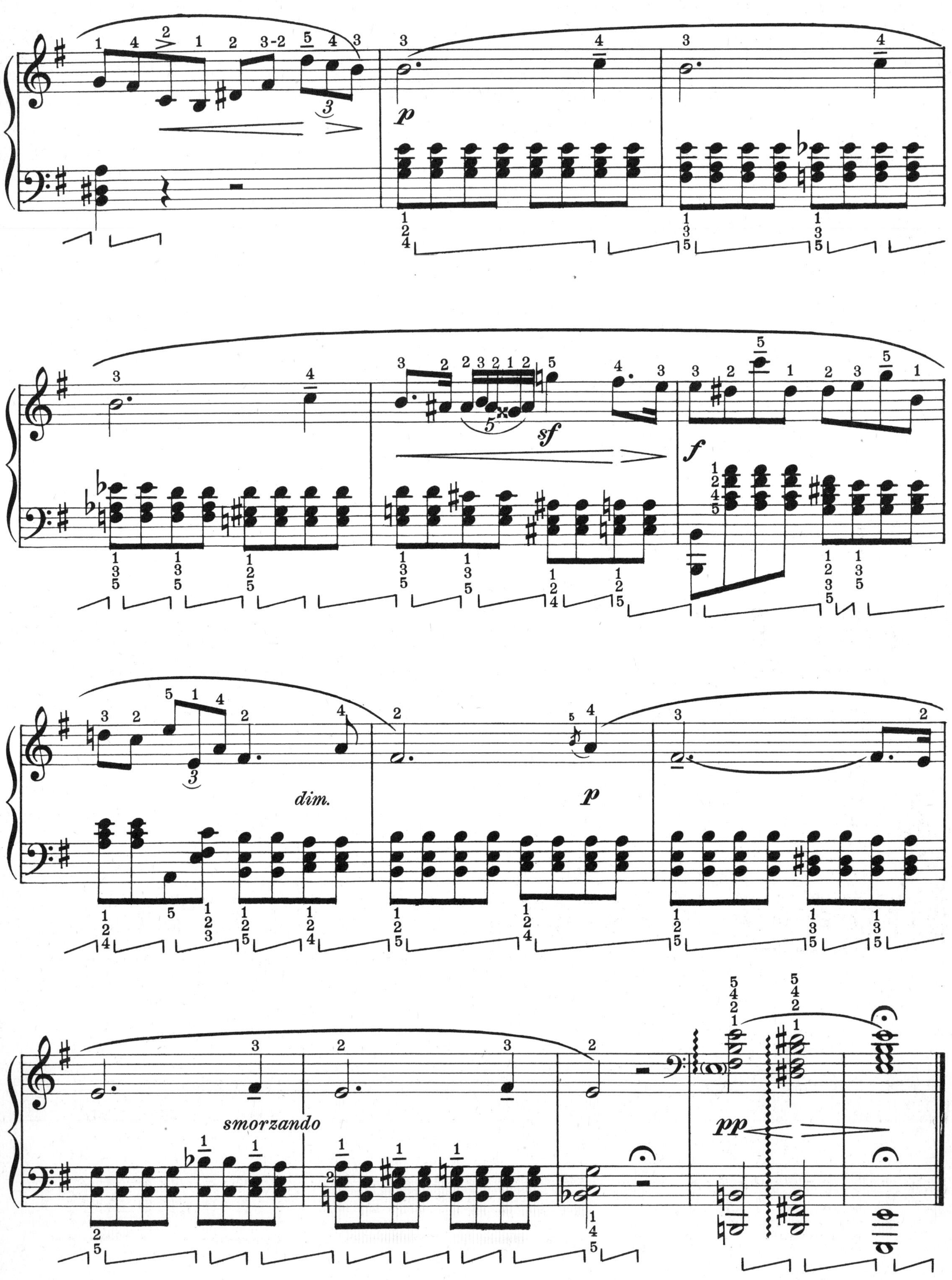
dim.
smorzando

This Trio movement is one of the best etudes for arpeggio study. With good, clean finger action, combined with skillful shifting of the hand and arm balancing on an alert, active thumb, play this number smoothly with no audible break in the tone as the hand moves from one octave to the next one.

TRIO FROM THE THIRD SONATA

Beethoven

D. C. al Fine

AIR IN G MAJOR

Handel

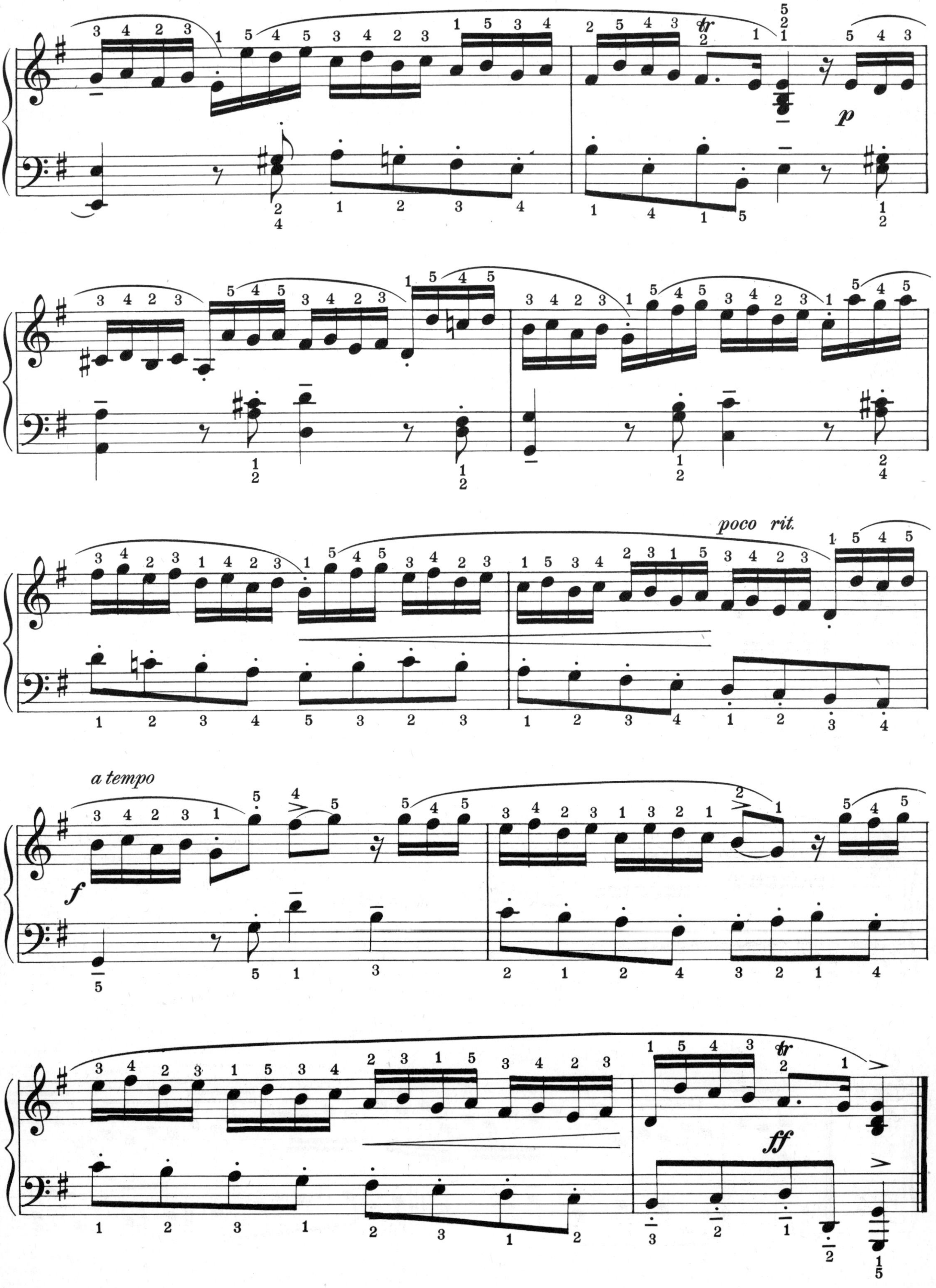
poco rit.
a tempo

Sir Edward Elgar was born at Broadheath, England, June 2, 1857 and died in 1934.   He is considered England's greatest musician since Purcell.   Elgar studied mainly by himself and in addition to mastering most of the instruments used in the orchestra, he also studied composition and taught music at the Birmingham Conservatory.   He composed much church music and orchestral pieces.

To play the piano with a deep, rich, sensitive singing tone, is the goal of every student. This number is one of the most exquisite of all melodies. Strive to make the piano sing this melody by means of a gentle, but heavy, arm touch for the single tones as well as the chord patterns in the right hand.

SALUT D'AMOUR
(LOVE'S GREETING)

Edward Elgar
Arranged by Bernard Wagness

a tempo
pochetto ritard.
p
p
mp cresc.
sfz
teneramente
poco agitato
fp

p cresc.
f
mp
molto cresc.
Tempo rubato
ritard. sffz
f
p cresc.
f molto ritard.

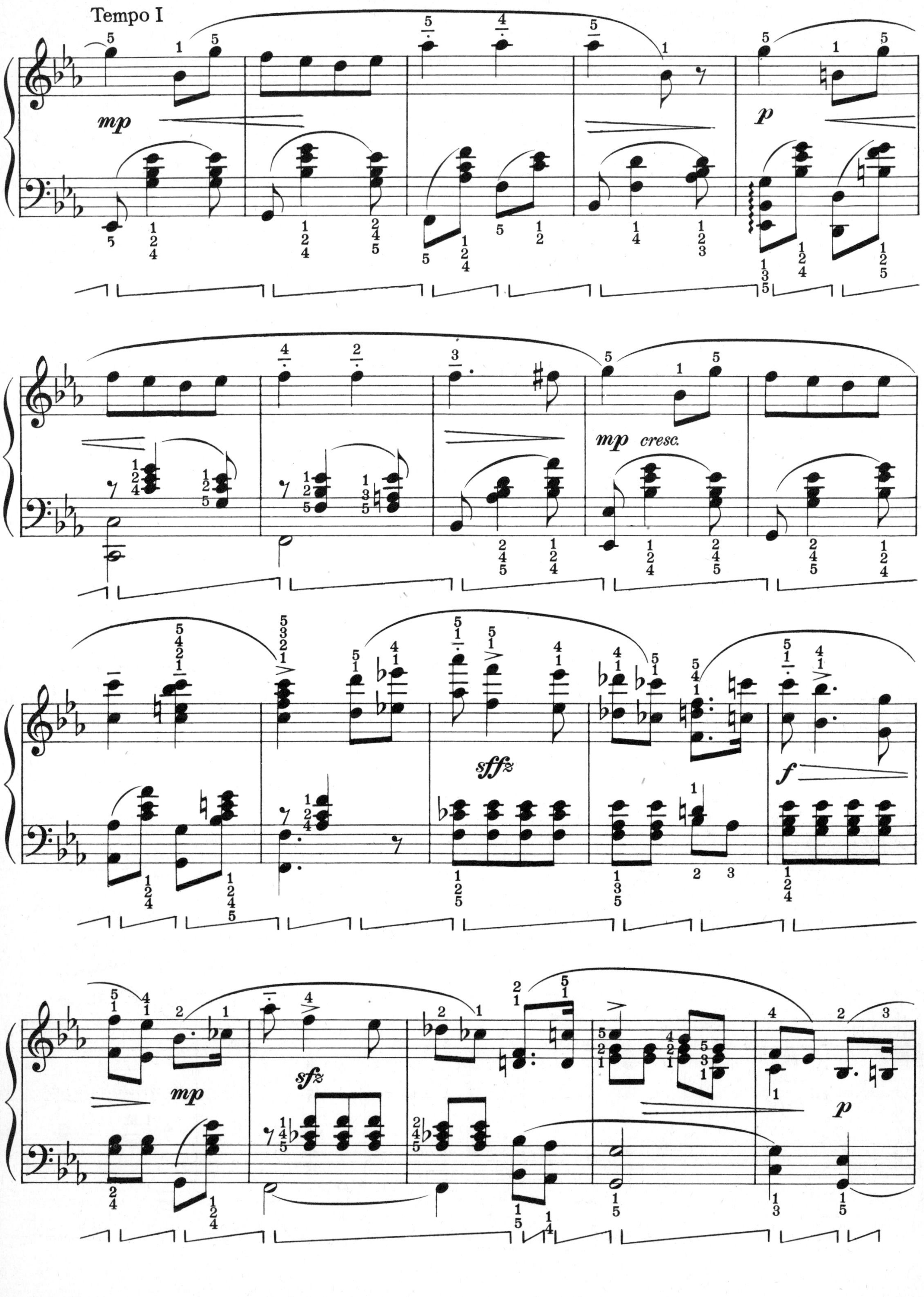
Tempo I
mp
p
mp cresc.
sffz
f
mp
sfz
p

cresc. e accel.
ff
largamente
sfz
mf
ritard.
Più lento
p
pp
pochetto rit.
a tempo
L.H.
pp

THE BLOCKING OF THE MAJOR SCALE

The blocking of the scale into solid groupings is to further impress the fingering through the tactile sense and to develop speed in playing scales. No speed in scale playing can be attained until the tactile sense can feel for groups of keys subconsciously.

Note: Play the hands separately.

To the teacher: This preliminary blocking of the scales with chord impressions will accustom the hand to readily shape and conform to each scale pattern. The hand thus held in diatonic readiness causes the fingers to fall naturally on the correct key.

A DIAGRAM FOR THE
BLOCKING OF THE MAJOR SCALES

Play hands separately until perfected.

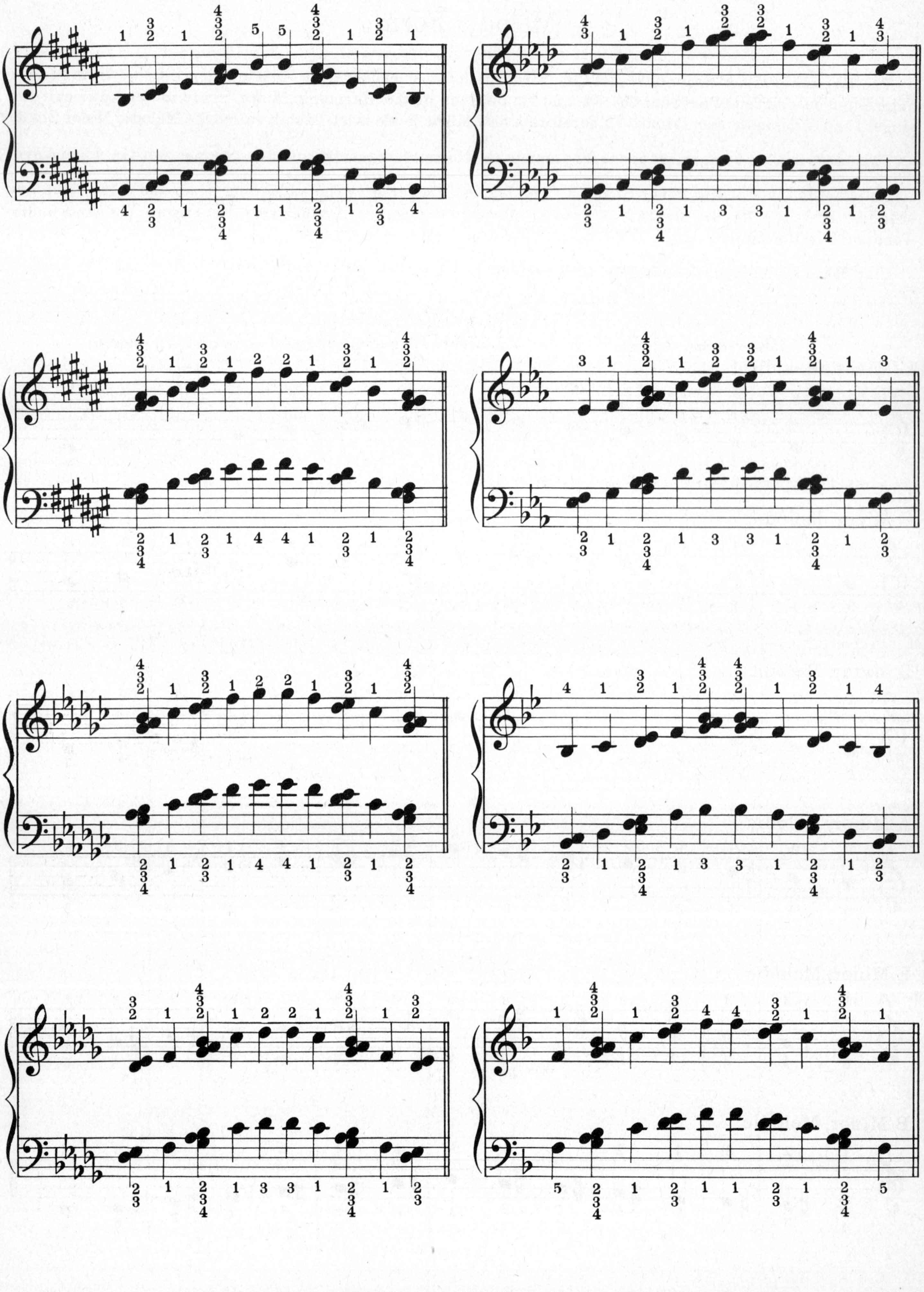

THE MINOR MODE
Melodic Form

The Harmonic Minor Scale provides the chordal material so necessary to music composition. However the augmented second found between the 6th and 7th degrees of the Harmonic Minor Scale is very difficult for singers and some instrumentalists. Therefore a new Minor Scale is introduced called the Melodic Minor Scale.

This scale is a very important one to all pianists as it is most frequently found in passage work in minor keys.

Note that in the Melodic Minor Scale the 3rd degree is lowered in the ascending scale and in the same descending scale the 7th, 6th and 3rd degrees are lowered one half step, otherwise it is exactly the same as it's Tonic or Parallel Major.

Play these scales hands separately until perfected.

F♯ Minor, Melodic

C♯ Minor, Melodic

C Minor, Melodic

F Minor, Melodic

B♭ Minor, Melodic

E♭ Minor, Melodic

A♭ Minor, Melodic

D♭ Minor, Melodic

G♭ Minor, Melodic

BROKEN CHORDS AND ARPEGGIOS

Transpose the following broken chords into all Major and Minor keys, each hand alone.

Transpose the following arpeggios into all Major and Minor keys. Connect well all crossings over and under the thumb. Refer to Figure A and observe the position of the thumb and second finger.

Figure A

For the Right Hand alone:

* The tied note must be given full value in order to provide a legato connection with the next octave group.

For the Left Hand alone:

* The tied note must be given full value in order to provide a legato connection with the next octave group.